RECKLESS BEGINNINGS

TAMMY MELLOWS TRILOGY BOOK 1

TINA HOGAN GRANT

Edited by Cat Chester of Pink Proof

Cover Design by T.E.Black Designs – http://www.teblackdesigns.com

1st printed in 2018 by Page Publishing

2nd printing 2021 by Tina Hogan Grant Books

❋ Created with Vellum

To My Mom & Dad

Dad you are missed every day.
Thank you for showing me the joy of books

Mom, you are the strongest woman I have ever known.
I follow in your footsteps with a zest for life and adventurous ways.

RECKLESS BEGINNINGS

BY TINA HOGAN GRANT

"Readers will be pulled in by the emotional intensity of the story. Tina Hogan Grant has a great sense of storytelling and she succeeds in keeping readers engaged through each page of her gripping story." - *Readers' Favorites*

"I started Reckless Beginnings at 10 pm last night and stayed up all night until I finished it at 8 am this morning, I was unable to stop and I loved it.

It is definitely a book to read, you will not be disappointed." *Amazon Reader*

"I loved this story, it was amazing!! It totally captured me from page 1 .After reading the first few chapters I was addicted and couldn't put the book down. I did nothing for the rest of the day." *Stewart Book Reviews*

"Reckless Beginnings has excellent character development, and Tina Hogan Grant does a fabulous job of showing the heartbreak of being involved with a drug addict. Compelling, heart-rending read. Couldn't put it down." *Michele L. Khoury Author of Busted*

PROLOGUE

ammy, the youngest of three sisters, remembered the phone call as if it were yesterday, even though it was almost three years ago, back in 1977. She was fourteen at the time and had already gone to bed when the ringing from the phone downstairs stirred her from her rested state.

She immediately knew it was her father, John calling from the United States. No one else phoned in the middle of the night. He had moved there shortly after her parents' divorce, accepting a job promotion he couldn't refuse as a speaker on artificial intelligence, and now lived on the outskirts of Boston. He had always called late on Thursday evenings because of the time difference between America and England. But, on that particular night, he called on a Tuesday—which had Tammy concerned.

Her parents had divorced when she was eleven because of her father's extramarital affairs. Tammy would never forget the day her family became divided. Like every morning, she had come downstairs wearing her pajamas. The house was silent except for the faint sound of crying coming from the front living room.

Tammy tiptoed softly toward the slightly open door and peeked in. Her heart ached with what she saw.

It was her mother, Rose; she had heard crying. She was sitting alone on the green couch with her hair in a tangled mess, wearing her pink satin bathrobe and holding a tissue to her eyes.

Fear swept over Tammy. Why was her mother so upset? She wanted to rush in and hold her and tell her everything was going to be okay. But Tammy felt her mother needed to be alone in her thoughts and stepped away from the door without being heard. Not trusting her older twin sisters, Donna and Jenny, to be quiet, Tammy decided to keep what she had seen to herself.

Later that morning, Tammy's questions had been answered. In a more composed state, their mother gathered her three girls into the family room. Still dressed in her bathrobe, her hair uncombed and her eyes swollen from her many tears, she held Tammy and her sisters tight. In a soft, broken voice she told them that she and their father were separating and that he had moved out of the house.

Crushed by the news, Tammy and her sisters clung to their mother, unable to control their tears. She had friends in school that came from broken homes and had listened with pity to their stories of violence and hatred before the divorce. They had told her how they hated spending weekends and holidays with only one parent. Was this how it was going to be for her? Tammy wondered.

Tammy was thankful she never saw violence, but she was devastated that her father was simply gone. No explanation, no goodbye, no hugs of reassurance that everything was going to be okay. She had felt abandoned and unimportant. How could he just leave without saying goodbye? When would she see him again? She had so many unanswered questions. Why did this happen? Why didn't they love each other anymore? Whose fault was it?

Unable to hold it together for her daughters, Rose was an

emotional wreck. The man she had loved for almost two decades was no longer in her life, and she was terrified of being alone.

Left in a garbage bag on the steps of an orphanage when she was six days old, where she remained until she was sixteen, Rose realized John had brought stability and a sense of belonging into her life for the first time.

She had met John in London on a bus on her way to the hotel where she worked as a chambermaid. John was on his way to college where he studied electronic engineering. The attraction had been mutual. He was infatuated with her beauty and her perfectly toned body. Rose was mesmerized by his handsome looks. His strong, defined jawline and his short, thick black hair that swept away from his face. Sitting across from her, he made her laugh and sometimes blush with his cheeky grin and the occasional wink directed solely at her.

John was a man with a brilliant mind. Rose admired him for his superior intelligence and his ambitious work ethics. In his younger years and straight out of college, John worked hard and was recognized for his achievements, becoming highly successful in the field of artificial intelligence. He spent his evenings working on his other passion, writing, with the hopes of being published someday.

His plans hadn't included becoming a father to twin girls at the young age of twenty, and then again to Tammy at almost twenty-three. Refusing to let fatherhood get in the way of his career, John became the sole provider, traveling a lot and leaving Rose to raise their daughters.

Eventually, his hard work had paid off and he managed to buy the family a beautiful four-bedroom home in the small, quaint northern English town called Tridale, which had lots of charm and history dating back to the Roman era. It was located on the valley floors of the Dales, surrounded by moors and rolling hills laced with heather and bracken.

John had been the backbone of the family. Everyone looked up to him. He provided structure and discipline; he set the ground rules and enforced daily chores for Tammy and her sisters.

The divorce hit each of the girls differently. Tammy missed having the authority figure of her father in the house. Jenny blamed him for abandoning them and became extremely protective and close to their mother. Meanwhile, Donna blamed both parents and began to travel down a road of self-destruction, wearing heavy makeup and skimpy clothes and drinking copious amounts of alcohol. For Rose, it was a constant battle, and she feared Donna was spiraling out of control. No longer able to handle her, Rose discussed Donna's behavior with their father and between them, they decided she might be better off with him.

For the next three years following her parents' divorce, Tammy spent her six-week summer vacations in America with her father and Donna. She and Jenny hated Donna being so far away. They talked once a week on the phone, but it wasn't the same. The sisters' bond had been broken.

Tammy and Donna reconnected each summer, but Jenny couldn't get past the grudge she held towards her father for breaking up the family. And, because she chose to stay in England with her mother during those summers, she began to grow apart from not only her father but also Donna.

Moving Donna to the States hadn't helped. For the next three years, she continued to act in a destructive manner, skipping school most days and spending her time drinking and hanging out with bad company. John suspected she was also using drugs. Unable to control his daughter anymore, he was at his wit's end and didn't know what to do.

Arrested one night for under-age drinking, Donna was escorted home in a patrol car. John expressed his concerns about his daughter's behavior with the officer, and they decided between them it might be better for her if she was placed into a juvenile home until she turned eighteen.

At the time, she was seventeen, which meant she would only be there for a year. John thought it was a good idea—after all, a year wasn't that long—and he pursued it the following day. Without having discussed it with Rose first, he found an all-girls home for troubled teens called *New Beginnings*.

A week later, after Donna was settled, he called Rose and explained to her that their daughter was out of control and needed professional counseling and guidance; something he couldn't give her. With the thought of her daughter being in a home tearing at her heart, Rose protested and objected to his decision, but it did no good. John was comfortable with his solution and the choices he'd made.

Within three weeks of Donna being admitted, John received a phone call from the director, telling him Donna had run away and couldn't be found. John had intentions of visiting her soon, but now that his book had finally been accepted for publication, he had been spending every spare moment trying to reach the deadline and the days had turned into weeks. The director went on to tell him that she had never really settled in. She rarely talked to the other girls and spent many hours sitting alone in isolated corners. She mentioned they had called and left numerous messages regarding Donna's behavior, but he had never returned their calls. John remembered those messages; there were three of them. He had planned on calling back after the deadline.

After apologizing profusely, Susan, the director, informed John that they had never had a child run away before and suspected Donna had left through the kitchen door, where the staff come and go and deliveries were made. She added that they pride themselves in providing an excellent home for all their children and emphasized again that Donna was the first case of a runaway.

John appreciated her sincere apology and had no harsh feelings. The only person he felt anger toward was himself. An unhappy seventeen year old would always find a way to leave if they really wanted to. No one was to blame but himself. He had selfishly ignored his troubled daughter's cry for help.

The lady on the phone told him the authorities had been notified and if they had any news, he would be informed immediately. John thanked her, hung up the phone and even though it wasn't Thursday—his day to call—he knew he had to tell Rose and reluctantly dialed her number.

Tammy had gotten good at eavesdropping on her parents' weekly conversations without being detected. She remembered on this particular Tuesday night how she quietly peeled back her sheets and tiptoed barefoot across her bedroom. Pinning her ear to the door, she heard her mother's voice echoing in the foyer below. Holding her breath, Tammy slowly pulled down on the door handle, praying the door wouldn't squeak when she eased it open. Thankfully, it had not, and Tammy released a sigh of relief. The light from the foyer lit up the landing outside her room, allowing her to find her way to the top of the stairs. Without making a sound, she had taken her usual spot on the last stair, pulled her white nightgown over her knees to keep out the chill, and peered down between the railings.

Her mother was dressed in her usual nighttime attire: a pink bathrobe, matching slippers, and her hair pulled back into a ponytail. Her back faced Tammy. Grateful her mother and father had remained friends after the divorce, their calls were usually pleasant, filled with jokes and laughter, but this phone call was different. Her mother sounded scared. Tammy sensed the fear in her voice. Only hearing one side of the conversation, Tammy had a hard time understanding what they were talking about. She only heard the strange questions her mother was asking.

"What do you mean she's gone, John?"

Who was gone? Tammy wondered.

Her mother became angry. "She can't just disappear, John! Someone must know where she is!"

Glued to the railings, Tammy was dying to know who and what they were talking about.

Then her mother began to cry hysterically while she held the phone tight and screamed into it, "She's still a child, John. She's just seventeen. You should never have put her in that home! She isn't an object you can just discard because she's in your way. She's your daughter!"

Tammy remembered how her heart sank to the floor when she suddenly realized they were talking about Donna. Her sister had run away and was now missing. She wanted to race down the stairs and snatch the phone from her mother's hands and ask her father WHY? Why had he put her in that awful place?

Donna had written a letter to Tammy and Jenny, telling them how much she hated being in the home. How no one wanted her anymore and she was going to run away. Frightened by what she had read, Tammy showed the letter to their mother. As upset as she was by both the letter and the fact that Donna had written to her sisters and not her, Rose never believed Donna would actually run away. "I'm sure she'll be okay. She just needs time to adjust. It's all new to her. We have to trust your father's judgment. He said this would be good for her. I have to believe that. She is a very troubled young girl and needs help," her mother had told her. But she had run away, and now no one knew where she was.

After spending her first summer in the States, Tammy had known she wanted to someday live there. Now since the disappearance of Donna, she wanted it more than ever. She needed to know what had happened to her. Waiting for the authorities to call wasn't enough. She needed answers. Why hadn't Donna contacted any of them? Was she in trouble? Was she hurt? Tammy didn't even want to consider her worst fear. The fear that maybe she was dead

CHAPTER 1

*T*ammy last saw her father two years ago when she was fifteen. He had managed to squeeze in a short two-day visit to England while on a book tour, but other than that, he had apparently been too busy for her to visit the States during the summer holidays.

At that time, it had been a year since Donna's disappearance and there was still no trace of her. No matter how much Tammy pleaded with her father to allow her to move to America, he had always come up with a different excuse. His latest was: she needed to finish school in England.

They had been sat at a small round table in a quaint English tearoom when he told her about his latest reasoning. Tammy's seat was next to a large picture window that looked out onto a busy street, clustered with many shops, restaurants, pubs, and people eager to spend their money. They were having lunch before he left the next day for his return trip home. His visits were always the same: short and rushed. Staying for just a few days, with never enough time for Tammy to persuade him to let her move to the

States. His work as an author engulfed him entirely, leaving little time for anything else. When he wasn't writing, he was traveling the world promoting his book or doing research for the next one.

Sitting across from him with her back to the window, she had her arms folded high across her chest, expressing her disappointment with pursed lips and sullen frown when she was once again told "no" in a stern voice by her father.

"I just don't understand why I can't go to school in America. It's just the same over there," Tammy argued.

Frustrated, John rolled his eyes at his daughter. "No, it's not the same, Tammy, and I've explained this to you repeatedly. The schools in England are far better than those in the States, and are you aware that students over there do not graduate until they're eighteen? Whereas here in England; it's only sixteen. Do you honestly want to be in school for another two years?"

Tammy thought for a moment. "Not really. But if it means I can live in the States, then I'm willing to make the sacrifice."

Even though John had been living in the States for a few years, he still had a thick British accent, which usually became more pronounced when he was angry. "Enough of this nonsense, Tammy. My mind is made up. You're to complete school over here, then, and only then will we discuss you moving to the States." He scowled at her from across the table and, without saying another word, looked down at his food, picked up his fork, and continued to eat his meat and potato pie in silence.

Tammy was tired and frustrated by his excuses. He used to say it was because she was too young or because he was too busy, and now it was because of school. When he first moved to the States, he had promised her that one day she would be able to move out there with him, but he had always found a reason for it to never happen.

She pleaded with him in an annoying, childish tone. "But I've lived here all my bloody life! I want a change and I want to live with you. I'm so tired of living here. There's absolutely nothing here for me. You know how much I love it over there."

John was beginning to lose his patience with his daughter. They went through this every time he visited. He saw the shock on her face when he raised his voice at her. "You're only fifteen years old, for God's sake! You have your whole life ahead of you. There's plenty of time for you to move to the States. If that's what you truly want in a few years, we'll discuss it then, understood?"

As hard as she pleaded, she knew he had made his decision and it was final. She was to finish her schooling in England. Two more bloody years of being unable to look for any clues or leads as to the whereabouts of her sister. It upset her tremendously. What if she was in danger? A lot could happen in two years. She hated not knowing.

She needed to know something. Anything. She couldn't wait until she was legally an adult. But, at least by then, no one could tell her what she could or couldn't do.

That was the last time Tammy had seen her father. She was now seventeen and living in her own flat in the northern city of Leeds. Donna still hadn't been found. If she were still alive, she'd be twenty years old. Tammy had to believe she was. She couldn't bear the thought that she might be dead.

Her flat was a place of convenience. Somewhere to eat, sleep, and bathe. She had made no efforts to make it feel like a home. The walls were white and bare with no pictures or decorations. She had little furniture; just the basics to get her by: a bed, chairs, couch, table, a TV, and a few bookshelves. She would make her real home in America.

Tammy didn't know how, but some way, she was going to get to the States. She'd lost faith in her father helping her. For the past five years, he had point blank refused her requests. But the pay of a waitress wasn't much and didn't go far. After paying her monthly bills, she had little left over for the so-called *America Fund*.

After completing school, she was anxious to leave home and took a job in the restaurant of a five-star hotel, working mainly nights. The job required no previous experience or special training, and she was hired the same day. Tammy figured she could always look for a better job later, if she was still in the country. But, for now, it was a way to make her own money and begin saving for her move to the States.

While still in England, nothing in her life could be permanent. Even her boyfriend Ian; whom she'd met three months ago at a disco. It was his dancing that caught her attention. He danced exceptionally well and wasn't afraid to dance alone. He was somewhat attractive, but if it weren't for his moves on the dance floor, she'd probably never have noticed him. His hair was dusty brown and cut short. She'd never really liked short hair on a man, but it suited him. He was a little bit taller than her five-eleven frame and skinny for a man of his height. Like most English people, including herself, his skin was pale; almost the color of ivory, and his freckles were plentiful on his arms, the tops of his hands, and all across his nose and cheeks.

He noticed her smiling and swaying her hips to the beat of the music as she watched him from the edge of the dance floor. He returned the smile along with a playful wink. He turned his body toward her, moving it in a suggestive manner as he held out his hand, inviting her to join him, which she did.

That was the beginning of their causal relationship with no strings attached. That night, Tammy took him home to her flat, where they frolicked beneath the sheets until the sun came up. In the three short months they'd know each other, she still knew very little about him apart from the fact that he was a waiter at a tearoom and still lived with his parents. She didn't need to know anything else. It was the perfect relationship; when she needed a little bit of fun, he was just a phone call away, but she chose not to share with him anything about her plans to someday move to America. She had a mission, and nothing or nobody was going to stop her.

CHAPTER 2

*I*t came as no surprise to the family that Jenny was going to marry Stuart. It had been expected since they started dating in grammar school when she was just fifteen. Being the most domesticated of the three girls, Jenny wanted nothing more than to settle down, buy a house, and start a family.

Tammy was pleased to hear that her father would be attending the wedding. Her mother asked that she reserve him a room at the hotel where she worked, which Tammy happily did.

On the day of his anticipated arrival, Tammy paced around the restaurant nervously, still trying to do her job while waiting for the announcement that her father was in the building. She wasn't going to ask him if she could go back to America with him this time. She already knew what the answer would be. His stay would be brief, as usual—three days—enough time to arrive, spend the night, attend the wedding, and leave the next day. Nonetheless, she wasn't going to deny that it would be good to see him and catch up.

It was over six months ago when Tammy last spoke to her father on the phone; that's when she learned she had a new stepmother called Joanne and a two-month-old half-brother called Andrew. She had felt a tinge of jealousy toward her unknown new sibling. She had always enjoyed being the youngest child, using it to her advantage in her earlier years by bribing her older sisters when she busted them doing something they weren't supposed to be doing. She had often used her title as "the baby sister" for never getting accused of any wrongdoings. Her parents always believed she was just too young and innocent, but in most cases, she had to admit she probably was the guilty party. Whether it was for drinking from their father's gin bottle, stealing cigarettes from their parents, or using their mother's makeup, Tammy joyfully watched while her sisters took the blame for such deceitful actions. Even at seventeen, there was still something special about being the youngest child. So, now that she had a half-brother of over sixteen years her junior, her title, in her eyes, had been stolen. Tammy felt cheated.

Polishing silverware, Tammy's mind was consumed with a plethora of family issues when the deep voice of her boss, John-Pierre, the maître d' of the restaurant, called across the room. His loud, thick French accent snapped her out of her thoughts. "Tammy, your father's here. He's waiting for you in the bar."

Jean-Pierre was a typical Frenchman. Aged around mid-fifties, he was pudgy and round with fat rosy cheeks and a full head of jet-black hair. His thick black moustache covered his upper lip and curled up into little circles at the ends. Growing up in Paris, France, he'd worked at some of the finest restaurants before moving to England with his family four years ago to learn the English language.

"And please, make it quick. You're still on the floor for another hour," he added.

"Thanks, Jean-Pierre. I won't be long."

Always feeling nervous around her father and constantly seeking his approval, Tammy stalled to quickly run her fingers through her red hair and smooth out her polyester uniform, which consisted of a dark blue mid-length skirt and a white blouse. She remembered hearing the disappointment in his voice over the phone when she told him she was a waitress.

As Tammy walked toward the bar, she pictured her father sitting alone with a Guinness Stout in one hand and a cigarette in the other while fully concentrating on The Times crossword puzzle. She peered through the double glass doors before entering and spotted him immediately. The image of her father was exactly as she had predicted.

Slowly approaching him, she realized one thing was missing: the cigarette. In silence, she stood behind him for a moment, chuckling to herself that he wasn't aware of her presence. She gave him a gentle tap on the shoulder. "Hi Dad!"

Her father removed his glasses, turned his head in her direction, and gave her a big smile. "Tammy! Good to see you," he said, giving her a hug.

"You too, Dad. It's been a while. I couldn't help noticing that you're not smoking. Crossword puzzles and cigarettes always went together," she said jokingly. "Don't tell me you've packed it in?"

"Actually, yes, I did," he said with a hint of pride. "It's been about four months now. I guess we haven't talked on the phone in a while, huh? But, if I can do it, so can you," he said, nudging her arm.

Tammy was shocked. Never did she imagine her father would quit smoking. "Wow, Dad, that's brilliant! And you smoked a lot too. About two packs a day, right? How'd you do it? Cold turkey?"

"No, cold turkey proved too difficult, so I weaned myself off gradually. It took some time, but now I feel marvelous!" He gave her another nudge to the arm. "You really should give it a go, you know."

"Nah, I'm still young, Dad. I can wait a few more years. Besides, I enjoy them too much!" she said with a laugh before glancing down at her watch. "I'm terribly sorry, Dad, but I have to make this short. I'm still working, but I get off in about an hour. Will that crossword puzzle keep you busy till then? I can meet you back here after I've finished my shift."

"Sure, that's fine. I'm all checked in."

"Great! I'll look forward to it. We certainly have some catching up to do. I hear you've been traveling all over the world promoting your new book?" She checked the time once more. "Anyway, I really do have to get back to work before Jean-Pierre kills me." After a quick hug and a peck on his cheek, Tammy returned to the restaurant thinking how good it was to see her father again after such a long time.

CHAPTER 3

*N*ow older, her anger dissolved, Tammy accepted the fact that it wasn't up to her father to fulfill her dreams of moving to the States. So, after finishing her shift, Tammy spent the rest of the evening with him, catching up on family news. He explained how being a writer had become much more challenging with an eight-month-old baby in the house, and he told her all about her new stepmom and half- brother as Tammy smiled and laughed along at his stories. Tammy then dropped the bombshell question, which is when the conversation took on a more somber mood.

"Any news on Donna, Dad?"

"No, I'm afraid not. When I moved to Lonesridge in Northern California last year, I left my new address and phone number with the children's home and the police."

"I'm really scared that something bad may have happened to her. It's been three years since she disappeared and we haven't heard anything."

"I know, me too, Tammy. The police have nothing to go on. It's like she just vanished. No one has seen her, and no one recognizes her from any of the photos that were circulated. I also gave them your mother's new number when she moved to that house in London to be a nanny, and they have your number and Jenny's, too."

"Yeah, Mom loves working again. Apparently, the family is well off and they treat her like a queen. I guess our old house was just too big for her after we all moved out." Tammy suddenly had a thought. "You know, it just occurred to me that we *all* have new phone numbers since Donna disappeared. What if she's tried calling one of our old numbers? We'd never know it. What a frightening thought. She has no idea where any of us are." Tammy reached for her father's arm. "Dad, she's out there somewhere with no way of calling us to ask for help!"

He patted Tammy's hand. "I hope that's not the case. I have to tell myself every day that she's okay and there's a perfectly good explanation why she hasn't contacted any of us. You might not agree with me, but it's how I keep my sanity when it comes to Donna."

"I understand. I just miss her so much. I try not to have terrible thoughts, but the more time goes by, the harder it gets."

Her father leaned in and gave her a gentle hug. "I know. Let's hope that someday soon, she'll return to us safe." He paused and smiled. "On another note, I spoke to your mother yesterday. She told me she'd be arriving tomorrow."

"Yes, she's taking the train up early in the morning. She's going to stay with Jenny for the weekend and take a late train back on Sunday night. She's looking forward to seeing you, Dad. She was upset when she first heard about you marrying again, but she's okay with it now. It's great how you've remained friends."

"Your mother and I had three wonderful daughters together. I screwed up our marriage, and it's only thanks to your mother that we have any kind of relationship today. It's her you should thank."

It saddened Tammy that Donna would miss her twin sister's wedding. She often wondered how Jenny was coping with her disappearance. She rarely spoke about it. Maybe it was just too hard. Growing up, they looked identical. Both had long, straight brown hair, light blue eyes with short eyelashes, and a fair complexion. If you didn't know that Donna had a slight curl to her smile and was a little skinnier than Jenny, you wouldn't be able to tell them apart. And, like most mothers of twins, Rose always dressed them in the same outfits.

Before saying goodnight to her father, Tammy arranged to meet him in the lobby the next day at noon. It seemed much easier for Tammy than trying to give him directions to her place. From there, they would ride together in her father's rental car to the wedding.

Because they were saving to buy a house, Jenny and Stuart had chosen to have a small, simple wedding with family members and a few close friends, followed by a buffet at a local hotel. Jenny looked radiant in her beautiful white gown, carrying a delicate bouquet of white roses and peonies. Tammy felt a twinge of jealousy as she watched Jenny walk down the aisle to her soon-to-be husband, saying her vows, and beginning her new path in life with solid plans for the future. It was far more than she'd ever had.

With the wedding ceremony over, Tammy had a chance to catch up with her mother. It had been a few months since they'd last seen each other. She missed her mother and always cherished their time together. Dressed in a cream-colored, knee-length dress with matching pumps and purse, Tammy's mother still had a slim figure, as always, and looked much younger than her age. Her makeup was light and fresh and her blond hair glistened in the sun. Her eyes sparkled and she looked genuinely happy.

Tammy told her how great she looked and her mother chuckled and confided in her that she had a new boyfriend. Having only seen her mother with her father, and with no inclination that she had dated anyone since the divorce, Tammy was surprised by the news. It was going to take some time to adjust to the idea of her dating somebody else, but she was delighted for her and it brought comfort to Tammy, knowing her mother wasn't alone.

After the reception, Tammy's father mentioned he wanted to have a chat with her and Rose and suggested going to the bar at the hotel where he was staying. Tammy rode with her father while her mother stayed behind to say goodbye to the last of the lingering guests, promising she'd take a taxi to the hotel shortly.

An hour later, they regrouped at a quiet corner table in the hotel bar. After taking a sip of his Guinness, a cheeky grin appeared across John's face, directed solely at Tammy. He leaned back in his chair with his arms folded over his chest. "So, Tammy, what do you think about coming back to the States with me?"

Rendered speechless with her eyes wide open, Tammy froze. Repeating in her head what her father had just said. *Did he just ask me to go to America with him?* Still holding her glass in mid-air, unable to contain her excitement, she screamed, "What! Are you serious?"

Other customers stared in her direction, silently questioning her sudden outburst. In fear of spilling her drink, Tammy placed it on the table before jumping up from her seat and running over to her father to give him the biggest hug he'd ever had. She didn't need to think about her answer. "I would love to!" she squealed. "When do we leave? I'm ready right now!"

John laughed at his daughter's enthusiasm. "Now hold on a second, Tammy," he said, peeling her grip from around his neck. "There are some details we need to discuss first." He looked over at Rose and his smile quickly disappeared. "Like your mother, for instance," he mumbled under his breath.

Rose's eyes had narrowed and darkened immensely, pulling the skin tight across her flushed cheeks, and her lips drew into a thin line as she scowled across the table at her ex-husband. It suddenly occurred to him that he perhaps should have discussed his idea with her before asking Tammy, but it was too late now.

"Rose, are you okay with this?" John asked, a look of guilt painted across his pale face.

Rose sat up straight and rolled her shoulders back. She wanted to make him feel uncomfortable. He was wrong to ask Tammy to move with him at such short notice, especially with no prior mention to her of his ridiculous idea. "Well, it's quite a shock, John. You never mentioned taking Tammy back with you until now. Don't you think that's a little unfair? Why hadn't you talked to me about this earlier instead of surprising me like this? You know I'll never see her again if she moves to the States. Look what happened to Donna. No one has seen or heard from her since she left with you. She could be dead for all we know."

John shook his head impatiently. "Oh, don't talk like that!"

"Well, she could be. We don't know. It's been three years since anyone has heard from her. I'm not losing another daughter, John." Her voice raised a notch with every word. She was almost on the verge of tears.

Tammy walked over to her mother. "Oh, come on, Mom, don't be like this. I'll keep in touch and I'm not going to disappear, I promise," she pleaded as she wrapped her arms around her mother's shoulders.

Rose looked up and met Tammy's eyes. "But when will I see you again? I can't afford to fly to the States every year to come visit you." John quickly raised his arms to calm them both down. "Okay, guys, let's not get ahead of ourselves here. This could just be a trial. She may not even like it in the States and may very well choose to move back to England."

"Not bloody likely," Tammy whispered under her breath.

John paused for a moment. He was walking on eggshells and needed to find a way to please them both. Choosing his next words carefully, looking directly at Rose, he said, "If she likes it, I promise I'll send you a ticket to come visit her. If she doesn't, then I'll buy her a ticket to return home and provide for her until she finds a job. How would that be?"

A silence descended over the table while Rose contemplated John's suggestion. Tammy and her father held their breath with anticipation. Both thought it was a good plan, but it seemed Rose had the final say.

After a few moments, Tammy grew impatient. "Oh, come on, Mom! What do you think? We'll still see each other. Please, Mom, just say yes. You know how much I've wanted this...and for so long. Please say yes. Please!" she begged while squeezing her mother's hand tight.

With a moment of hesitation, Rose gave them her decision. "Okay, Tammy, I guess you can go." She didn't want to see the disappointment on her daughter's face if she'd said no. In the same breath, Rose quickly turned, pointed her index finger at John, and stiffened her voice. "You better take good care of her, John." Raising her voice, she continued to speak. "And don't you dare loose contact with her, like you did with Donna." She turned and looked at Tammy. "And you must promise me, Tammy, that you'll write to me every chance you get."

Rose felt her body tremble as she hugged her youngest child. Was she doing the right thing by allowing yet another daughter to move so far away to another country? Silently, she blamed John. If it wasn't for him moving to America in the first place, she wouldn't be having this conversation or having these fears, and Donna would still be in their lives. With tears in her eyes, Tammy hugged her mother tight and promised to write as often as she could. She couldn't believe she was finally going to America!

CHAPTER 4

*A*fter the initial shock had sunk in and her mother had been persuaded that everything was going to be okay, the rest of the evening was spent discussing the move.

Overjoyed and riddled with excitement, Tammy couldn't believe this was finally happening. On the contrary, it warmed Rose's heart to see such a joyous smile on her daughter's face. Even though she was going to miss Tammy deeply, she was truly happy for her. She knew in her heart it was time to stop being selfish and, perhaps more importantly, it was time to let her go.

John told them he would be in England for another week. He was leaving tomorrow to go down south to Surrey to visit his sister, Maddie, and his brother-in-law, Dave. While there, he would purchase Tammy's plane ticket and she could take the train down at the end of the week. They would then leave from Heathrow Airport in London the following Monday.

Tammy soon realized she had a lot to do in just seven days. She had to decide what she wanted to take with her. The airline would only allow her to take one suitcase, which meant she would have to donate the rest of her things to charity or give them to friends at work. She also needed to give notice to her landlord and her manager at work. Sadly, she realized she wouldn't be able to say goodbye to Jenny. She would still be on her honeymoon on the day of her departure. Tammy had no doubt Jenny would be crushed, but what could she do? She was afraid if she didn't go now, her father might never ask her again.

With so much to do in so little time, the week flew by quickly. When Tammy wasn't working, she spent every spare moment going through her belongings, deciding what to keep and what to part with. She had friends from work coming by every day, taking the things she no longer wanted such as clothes, dishes, records, books, and furniture. Where had all this stuff come from? She never realized how much junk she'd accumulated.

Tammy knew she was going to need to set a day aside for the three-hour train ride to Surrey and so gave five days' notice to her landlord and her job. She appreciated their understanding and both expressed how excited they were for her. Everyone at work was truly happy for her. Some even confessed how envious they were and most agreed they needed to get together for a going away party. It wasn't every day someone from work was moving to America, they proclaimed.

By the end of the week, Tammy had managed to get rid of most of her possessions, except for the bed, which she planned on leaving behind. With all her dishes gone, she was now eating only take-out meals—it was as good an excuse as any to live on junk food for a few days. Her one suitcase was packed with clothing, toiletries, a few photographs, and a few of her favorite books.

Tonight was going to be her last night at work. Tomorrow, she would be taking the train down to Surrey to meet up with her father. She couldn't believe how fast the week had gone by and yet, to her surprise; she had managed to check off everything on her list. Tammy was ready for her big move to the States.

There was no turning back now. Deep down, she was extremely nervous and couldn't deny the anxiety bubbling away in her stomach. England had been her only home. She would be leaving behind so much, including her mother, sister, and friends. She would no longer have a home to call her own and would have to find new restaurants and shops to call her favorites. After the move, the only people she will know will be her father and his wife Joanne, whom she had yet to meet. Tammy questioned if they would get along and, at times, even questioned if she was doing the right thing by leaving her whole life behind.

When Tammy arrived at work, Jean-Pierre told her that he had to change the schedule, so she was now going to be closing the restaurant at eleven instead of getting off at nine. Tammy couldn't hide her anger. "Jean-Pierre, how can you do this to me? You know it's my last night," she shrieked while stomping her feet in protest. "I was hoping to go out after work. I won't get another chance!"

"Oh, stop with your whining, Tammy," he snapped in his fancy French drawl. "It couldn't be prevented. Someone called in sick. What was I supposed to do? I know it's your last night and I'm sorry." He placed his hand on her shoulder. "Tell you what. Because I feel so awful about this, why don't you let me buy you a drink at Danny's pub after work?"

Having calmed down after her initial outburst, and having no actual plans, Tammy accepted his invitation.

Ten o'clock couldn't come fast enough. It had been a busy night for the restaurant, and even though it was now closed, it would still take Tammy another hour to shut everything down before her shift was officially over. During her last hour, co-workers approached her to wish her well and say their goodbyes before leaving for the evening. Some even brought tears to her eyes with their heartfelt farewells.

By eleven o'clock, she was the only one left. So much for a leaving party, she thought. The only task remaining was to turn off the lights. But, as Tammy stood by the switch, she hesitated and took one last look around the restaurant as if capturing the memories she would be taking with her. That's when it hit her. It felt so real—she'd never see this place again. Not wanting to cry or become too emotional, she quickly turned off the lights, leaving only darkness behind her, and headed over to Danny's pub to meet Jean-Pierre.

CHAPTER 5

*A*fter putting on a sweater over her uniform, Tammy stepped outside into the cold, damp night, only to be greeted by pouring rain. "Well, what a bloody surprise," she mumbled to herself sarcastically. Rain was the one thing she wasn't going to miss about England. Feeling irritated because she no longer owned an umbrella, Tammy pulled her sweater over her head to keep her hair dry and ran across the deserted streets to Danny's pub. As she quickly scurried through the parking lot, she noticed it was full. "Wow, it's busy here tonight," she said while heading toward the entrance. When she reached the door, she saw there was a sign posted on it. Tammy squinted her eyes in the dim light and read the words out loud. "Closed for private party."

"Well, that's just bloody great!" she yelled in disgust and looked up. The sky was turning darker by the second, unleashing torrents of increasingly heavy rain that was pelting the ground under her feet. "Now what am I going to do? This is turning out to be a bloody horrible night!"

Tammy assumed Jean-Pierre had also seen the sign and gone home. Upset that the pub was closed on her last night, Tammy turned around and began walking back to the hotel so she could call a taxi to take her home. It looked like she was going to be spending her last evening alone. Dodging the ever-growing puddles as she hurried across the parking lot, she heard a male voice call her name.

"Tammy! Tammy! Wait!"

She stopped and turned around, still partly hidden underneath her sweater. She squinted her eyes through the darkness and craned her neck forward, trying to recognize who was calling her. She couldn't quite make out who it was. He was wearing a black overcoat and carrying a large black umbrella, which cast shadows over most of his face. As Tammy began to run toward him, the familiar silhouette of Jean-Pierre came into focus.

Puzzled, she ducked under his umbrella and pulled her wet sweater back down over her head. "Jean-Pierre, why are you still here? There's a private party inside. Look," she said, pointing at the sign, "the pub is closed. I thought you'd already gone home. Do you want to go someplace else?"

"It's okay, they are letting the locals in. Come on, let us go inside, mon amie," he replied.

Feeling much better for knowing she wasn't going to be spending her last night alone, Tammy linked arms with Jean-Pierre and threw him a smile. "Let's go. I need that drink you promised me."

Once inside the pub, Tammy was amazed by how busy it was. Loud music was playing and people were dancing, laughing, and singing along to the music. Along one of the walls of the dance floor, she saw a buffet of delicious food. She felt like an intruder. This was a special party for someone, and she wasn't supposed to be here. That was until she noticed the large banner spanning across the room that read, "God help the U.S.A!" in large red, white, and blue letters.

Shocked, she quickly spun around in a circle, trying to focus on the people amid the haze of cigarette smoke and flashing disco lights. It took a moment to sink in, but she soon realized they were the faces of all her co-workers from the restaurant. With a hand over her gaping mouth, Tammy turned back to face Jean-Pierre. "Oh my god! This party is for me? It's a leaving party?" She still couldn't quite believe her eyes.

At that precise moment, everyone turned to face Tammy and yelled, "Surprise!" in unison while raising their glasses in her honor.

Jean-Pierre wrapped his arm around her shoulders and gave her a tight squeeze. Using his other hand, he handed her a glass of champagne from the table next to him. "For you," he said with a huge grin. "It's the drink I owe you."

Wiping the tears that were now rolling down her cheeks, Tammy took the glass of bubbly. "Oh my god, Jean-Pierre. How did you ever pull this off? This is just too weird! I had no idea you were planning this...I'm going to miss you all so, so much."

Jean-Pierre smirked. "Let me tell you, it was not easy. You are a hard one to keep a secret from. Now do you see why I had you close the restaurant? I had to make sure you were the last to arrive. I am sorry if I upset you, mon amie, but as you can see, my intentions were good." He laughed as he hugged her one more time and raised his glass. "Here's to you, Tammy. I wish nothing but the best for you and your new life in the States. We are all going to miss you incredibly. Especially that redhead attitude of yours that always kept us on our toes."

Tammy hugged him back. "Awe, thanks, Jean-Pierre. I'm going to miss you too." They walked arm in arm toward the bar where everyone was gathered. Feeling like a celebrity and overwhelmed with different emotions, she made a point of greeting everyone with a tearful hug.

Tammy spent the rest of the night hugging, laughing, and dancing with friends. Many tears were shed, memories were shared, and promises were made. Everyone seemed to want to know what plans she had for when she landed in the States, but she genuinely had no idea and replied she would figure it out once she got there.

As the night drew to a close, Jean-Pierre held a shot of tequila, took Tammy's hand, and led her to the center of the room. Everyone else grabbed their glasses and followed them. Jean-Pierre waited while the crowd formed a circle around him and Tammy. Feeling a little tipsy, Tammy could feel her emotions beginning to rise again. She squeezed Jean-Pierre's hand harder, feeling the dam of tears in her eyes threatening to burst at any moment.

The crowd stood in silence, waiting for Jean-Pierre to make his speech. He turned to Tammy, giving her a warm, loving smile. "Tammy may all your dreams come true in America. It's not going to be the same here without you. Be good to America and it will be good to you. We will truly miss you and we love you. Bon voyage!" Sweeping his raised glass in an arc toward the circle of friends, he added at the top of his voice, "To Tammy!"

Everyone lifted their glasses and bottles in the air and yelled in reply, "To Tammy!" She embraced Jean-Pierre with force, staying in his arms for a moment as an uproar of applause and cheers filled the pub. Unable to control her tears, she allowed them to fall freely down her freckled cheeks as her lips trembled and her body shook with the burden of her imminent departure.

As the pub began to empty, Tammy said goodbye to the last of her friends and fought to bring her emotions back under control. Jean-Pierre then called for a taxi to take Tammy home. When it arrived, she once again thanked Jean-Pierre for everything. Noticing she was unsteady on her feet, he took her arm and walked her out to the waiting car. As it began to pull away, Tammy turned her head to look through the rear window. Seeing Jean-Pierre still standing by the curb, she gave him one last wave, knowing it would be her last.

Once inside her flat, still feeling a little drunk, Tammy knew she had one more thing to do. Something she had been avoiding all week but knew she could no longer put off. Even though it was almost three o'clock in the morning, the alcohol she had consumed was giving her the courage to finally get it done. Taking slow and careful steps so as not to stumble, she managed to totter over to her bed, sit on the edge and pick up the phone that was lying on the floor. The dial tone meant the phone company had not yet disconnected her services. She wasn't sure if she was relieved or disappointed to hear it. After she dialed the number, it rang three times before a sleepy voice answered. "Hello," it said in a questionable tone.

She took a deep breath. "Hi, Ian, it's Tammy."

Ian instantly woke up. "Tammy! Where've you been? I've not seen you all week. I've called you millions of times, but you've never called me back."

"Yeah, I know. I'm sorry, I've been really busy."

"Is everything okay?" Ian asked.

"I'm so sorry to be calling you at this hour, but there's something I need to tell you."

"Couldn't it have waited till morning?"

"I'm afraid not." There was a moment of silence between them while she hesitated.

"Tammy, you still there?"

"Yes, I'm still here, Ian." She took another deep breath. "It can't wait till morning because I won't be here."

"You won't be here? What do you mean you won't be here? What's going on?"

"Ian, there's no easy way to say this so I'm just going to come out and say it. I'm moving to the States with my dad. I leave tomorrow. I'm meeting him at my aunts in Surrey. I've been wanting to tell you, but I just didn't know how. Please don't be mad at me."

"You're moving to the States? And you're telling me this now, in the middle of the night, just hours before you're fucking leaving!

What about us, Tammy? What about your job and flat? Doesn't anything matter to you? Including me?"

She decided she needed to be honest with him. "Ian, I've known for a week. Since my father asked me. I've already quit my job, and my flat is empty except for one suitcase. This is something I've wanted for a long time so when he asked me, I just couldn't say no. I don't know if he'll ever ask me again and I'm not giving up this chance. I'm sorry, Ian, I don't know what else to say."

"But what about us, Tammy?" Ian asked again.

"I hate to say it, Ian, and I'm truly sorry, but it's over. We've only been dating for a short while and we both knew it wasn't serious. But, for me, moving to the States *is* serious. I'm sorry if I've hurt you in any way, but my mind is made up. This is the reason I haven't told you up until now. I didn't want you to try and talk me out of my decision."

Ian couldn't believe what he was hearing. "But you just left me totally in the dark. I thought I deserved better than this. I wondered why I hadn't seen you all week, or why you hadn't returned my calls. So, that's it, eh? Just like that. Poof! You're gone." He continued to speak; the anger and frustration clear in his voice. "I agree that we were just having some fun, but we were friends, Tammy. Well, at least, I thought we were. So this is how you treat your friends, eh?"

"I said I was sorry. What more do you want me to say?"

"What time are you leaving in the morning? Can I at least see you before you go? I deserve that much, don't I?" He was almost snarling down the phone.

Tammy didn't blame him for being angry. She felt awful, mainly because she'd actually grown quite fond of him. "I'd much rather you didn't. As difficult as this is, I think it's best we just end it tonight." She could feel the tears glazing over her eyes. Not wanting him to hear her cry, she spoke with a sense of urgency. "Ian, I really have to go. I need to get up early. It's been nice knowing you and I had a lot of fun. I'll never forget you. Be safe, Ian, and goodbye."

Before he could answer, she quickly hung up the phone and yanked the phone line out of the wall socket. She feared he might try to call back in an attempt to convince her to stay. She knew he wouldn't show up at her door because, like her, he didn't drive, couldn't afford a taxi, and thankfully no buses ran in the wee hours of the morning.

After a night of painful goodbyes, Tammy's emotions were in turmoil. Feeling alone, insecure, and unsure of her future, she once again questioned the choices she was making in her life. With her head spinning and anxious for tomorrow to arrive, she lay on the bed and curled her body into the fetal position as if to protect herself from the inevitable. In no time at all, perhaps thanks to the alcohol, she drifted off to sleep.

CHAPTER 6

The next morning, an intense throbbing headache woke Tammy up from a deep sleep. She slowly pulled herself into an upright position and pivoted her legs over the edge of the bed. Despite the pounding in her head showing no signs of mercy, she needed to find strength to face the new day. Grasping her temples with both hands, she moaned out loud. "Oh God, why did I have so much to drink last night?"

Still in her now wrinkled uniform, which she no longer needed, Tammy slowly hoisted her limp, aching body to a standing position. With her eyes squinted, she tried to shut out the intensity of the bright daylight streaming through the bare window. With an almighty effort, she just about managed to raise her arm and look at her watch through narrowed, unfocused eyes. She saw it was ten o'clock and gasped. Her train to Surrey was departing in an hour!

"Oh crap! You have to get a move on, Tammy!" she hollered to herself in a rush of panic, drowning out any previous thoughts of hangovers and headaches. With no time to waste, Tammy quickly gathered up her jeans and t-shirt that she had purposely laid out on top of her suitcase the day before and fled the room to take a shower.

By ten thirty, and after a cold shower, she was dressed and feeling somewhat normal again. She picked up her suitcase and handbag and took one last look around her now empty flat. It had been home for almost two years. Now that it really was time to leave it, a weight of sadness pulled at her heart. "Farewell, flat, I'll miss you," she said softly before placing the key on the counter and heading out the door.

The train station was six miles away. Knowing there was no time to wait for a bus, Tammy opted to walk the few streets into town and grab a taxi instead. She arrived at the station with just ten minutes to spare. Thankful her father had purchased the ticket in advance, she scurried over to the ticket booth to pick it up. The elderly man behind the counter informed her that the train was on time and would be leaving from platform nine in five minutes.

With ticket in hand, she ran through the station as quickly as her old suitcase on frail, plastic wheels would allow. She reached the platform and checked in her luggage with the conductor before leaping on board the train to the sound of the final whistle for departure. Breathless but happy to find a window seat available, she plumped herself down in a state of exhaustion just as the train began to pull out of the station. This was it. Her journey to the United States had begun. She was finally on her way.

As the train gained speed, she watched through the window as her hometown faded off into the distance. With mixed emotions, she whispered, "Goodbye, Leeds. I'll come visit you again soon, I promise."

Still suffering from the previous night but delighted to have the double seat all to herself, Tammy lifted the arm to the adjoining seat and arranged her body comfortably by curling her legs up and resting her tired head against the window. She closed her eyes to block out the rays of the mid-morning sun gleaming through the window, and in no time at all, she drifted off into a deep sleep.

Images of her new life in the States painted themselves into her dreams; she was living in the big city—maybe it was New York—and she was driving a big American car. She was with friends and her sister Donna was with them too. She didn't know where they were going, but they all seemed happy. They were living the American Dream.

Stirring from her sleep, Tammy checked her watch, and re-checked when she realized she'd slept for most of the three-hour trip. Finally, the train pulled into the station and she quickly ran a brush through her hair and touched up her lipstick with her favorite color, Ruby Rose, before exiting and stepping onto the platform.

Scanning across the sparse gathering of people waiting at the small, quiet station, it was easy to spot her father waving in the distance by the green wooden benches. She beamed a radiant smile and waved both hands above her head in excitement as he began to walk toward her.

Spanning her shoulders with his arm, her father gave her a tight squeeze and a cheerful grin. "You made it!"

"I did," Tammy said with pride.

John loosened his grip so Tammy could turn to face him. "I wasn't sure if I would. I didn't realize how much there was to do in just a week, but I managed to get it all done...just! And here I am." Still smiling, she continued to tell him more. "Last night, my work threw me a brilliant leaving party. It was a total surprise!" She gasped, remembering her shock of everything from the night before. "I had no clue. I don't know how they pulled it off without me knowing, but they did."

"That's great! They must have liked you a lot to go to all that trouble. Sounds like they gave you a really good send off," John remarked while they stood waiting for her suitcase to be unloaded from the train. "You can tell me all about it when we're in the car. Aunt Maddie and Uncle Dave can't wait to see you."

"And I can't wait to see them! It's been a long time. I haven't seen them in ages...in fact, I don't think I've seen them since you and Mom got divorced."

"Well, looks like your suitcase is ready," her dad replied, pointing to the cartful of unloaded luggage. "Let me grab it for you and we'll make a move."

Smiling from ear to ear, Tammy replied, "Great, thanks. One step closer to America!"

CHAPTER 7

*I*t was only a fifteen-minute drive to her aunt and uncle's house. It looked exactly how she remembered it. They'd lived on the quiet cul-de-sac for more than twenty years. Raising two sons, Peter and Shawn, who now had families of their own, they'd lived the old-fashioned life, with Maddie staying at home to look after the boys while Dave worked to provide for the family. All the houses in the neighborhood were elegant detached family homes with immaculate well-maintained gardens. Her aunt's house, located at the end of the road, still had the white painted siding and black decorative shutters that Tammy remembered so well. The quintessential picket fence, still laced with white roses, brought her right back to her childhood days.

As they slowly pulled into the driveway, Tammy couldn't help but smile as she watched her aunt come rushing out of the front door and skip with joy down the three front steps. Trembling with excitement, she anxiously waited for them to exit the car. Tammy was delighted to see Aunt Maddie still looked the same and didn't appear to have aged much over the years. Still wearing her shoulder-length, sable-brown hair clipped away from her ever-youthful face, it was clear to see time had been good to her.

Aunt Maddie was most famous in Tammy's family for two things: her cooking and for always wearing brightly colored aprons. Today, she didn't disappoint, as she had chosen to wear a luminous pink apron with vertical red stripes. The minute Tammy stepped out of the car, Aunt Maddie squealed with delight and engulfed Tammy in her arms, holding her cheek to cheek while squeezing her tightly.

"My dear Tammy, it's so good to see you!"

"Hi, Auntie Maddie. It's good to see you too," Tammy managed to say, while still being smothered by her aunt's embrace.

Finally releasing her hold, Maddie took a step back while holding Tammy at arm's length. She took a good long look at her, inspecting her from head to toe, and smiled with pride. "Look at you. You're all grown up and so pretty. I just love your beautiful red hair," she said, combing it with her fingers. She turned her head in the direction of John, who was busy unloading Tammy's suitcase from the boot of the car. "She definitely has your Irish blood, John."

"What makes you say that?" John said sarcastically.

Maddie laughed. "Oh, give over, John. Still sarcastic as ever, I see." Pulling Tammy by her hand, she headed back towards the house. "Come on inside and let me fix you both something to eat. You must be starving after that long train ride."

"I'll be right in. You two go ahead," John replied.

Entering the house, Tammy's head was once again flooded with childhood memories. Nothing had changed. It was an open- plan home with no shortage of natural sunlight, thanks to the generous amount of windows. A white-tiled kitchen bar, complete with ornate wooden stools, separated the kitchen from the main living and dining area. Glass French doors from the dining room opened out onto a large brick patio, furnished with a round wooden table and chairs. The outdoor seating area was dressed with red and white floral cushions and shaded by a matching umbrella. Maddie's china collection, consisting of delicate teacups, teapots and plates, was displayed around the dining room on high wooden shelves, adding an essence of English charm to the decor.

In no time at all, Aunt Maddie got busy in the kitchen, doing what she loved best: entertaining and cooking. Tammy took a seat at the counter and engaged in cheerful conversation and laughter while her aunt glided around the kitchen with ease, fixing a hearty-looking lunch.

"I bet you're excited about moving to America. What a fantastic opportunity," Maddie remarked while slicing up some turkey.

"I am, but I'm a bit worried about Mom. I don't think she likes the idea."

"Oh, don't you worry about Rose. I'm sure she'll be just fine. Maybe a little lonely at times, but Jenny will be just a few hours away. Now, where is your dad? These sandwiches are almost ready."

After unloading the car and taking the suitcases upstairs, John joined them in the kitchen. Feeling famished, his eyes almost popped out of his head as he welcomed the oversized turkey sandwich that his sister placed before him.

With lunch devoured and stomachs filled, they took advantage of the pleasantly warm afternoon by relaxing outside on the patio.

Tammy thought back to all the Christmases spent at her aunt's house, when cousins, aunts, uncles and grandparents traveled from all corners of England to come together for the festive activities. It saddened her that many of the families from back then, including her own, were no longer together. All had gone their separate ways. Sadly, annual holiday gatherings were now something of the past.

Her daydream, was interrupted by her father.

"I meant to tell you this earlier, but I've not been able to get a word in edgeways with you and your aunt nattering all afternoon. Your mother is coming down tomorrow by train."

"She is?" Tammy replied excitedly. "Oh, that's fantastic! Auntie, when was the last time you saw my mom? It's been ages, hasn't it?"

"Oh my goodness, I'm not sure. But yes, it has been a rather long time," Maddie said, serving everyone a cup of tea.

"She'll only be here for the day. We'll have to pick her up from the train station in the morning," John stated.

"Oh, I can't wait to see her. It's going to be just like old times," Maddie said, clasping her hands together in joy.

Later that evening, Uncle Dave returned home from his life-time job as an insurance salesman. Tammy had never known him to do anything else. He hadn't changed much either, except for the few gray strands invading his light hazelnut hair, which he wore short and well trimmed. He was still the tall and lanky uncle with the prominent nose and sharp chin that Tammy remembered.

He set his briefcase on the floor at the bottom of the stairs and walked over to Tammy to give her a big hug. "Tammy, sweetheart, it's so good to see you! Hey, what happened? You're not a little girl anymore."

Tammy chuckled. "Good to see you too, Uncle Dave."

For dinner, Aunt Maddie treated everyone to some of her home- made cooking and filled their plates with roast beef, York-shire pudding, mashed potatoes, and gravy. Fresh-baked apple pie and custard followed for dessert. After the delicious meal, John and Dave retired to the den for what would probably turn into an intense game of chess. Both were brilliant chess players and no doubt eager to finally have a game against a challenging opponent. Tammy, tired from her trip and sensing it might be a long game, decided to leave them to it and called it an early night.

Anticipating the arrival of her mother was also weighing heavy on her mind, adding to her fatigue. Saying goodbye to her wasn't going to be easy, and Tammy was worried her mother may dissolve into an emotional wreck during their final farewell. Although she was expecting there to be some tears shed between them, she didn't want it to be any harder than it needed to be.

CHAPTER 8

*H*er mother's train arrived on time at precisely ten o'clock the following morning. Tammy and her father waited anxiously on the platform as they watched the train slowly pull into the station and come to a halt amid a billowing cloud of steam and smoke. Up until now, Tammy had been okay with saying goodbye to her mother, but as she stood waiting for her to exit the train, she could feel her levels of anxiety beginning to increase. First came the sweaty palms, then the butterflies churning through her stomach. Trying to sooth herself, she gently rubbed her belly in a circular motion. It didn't help. Instead, feelings of dizziness and nausea began to creep in, and her heart hammered against her ribcage.

It occurred to her that this wasn't going to be easy, even after living by herself for almost two years; her mother had always been just a train ride away. After tomorrow, she'll be six thousand miles away. No longer would she be able to simply jump on a train whenever she felt the need to visit her mother. Tammy had never realized how much she took her for granted: not until this moment.

Lost in her thoughts, Tammy suddenly spotted her mother stepping off the train and quickly changed her state of mind. "I can do this," she whispered to herself. She held her head an inch or two higher as if to convince herself it was all going to be fine.

She admired her mother from afar, dressed casual and looking good in blue jeans, a purple t-shirt, and black low-heeled pumps. She carried a black purse over her shoulder and a black cardigan hung loosely over her arm. Her mother had always taken pride in the good looks she was gifted with, and enhanced them perfectly with just the right amount of makeup. She never had a hair out of place and her nails were always beautifully manicured.

"There she is, Dad," Tammy said while waving to her mother.

Rose spotted them right away. She smiled and waved back. Tammy took a deep breath and exhaled just as sharply before walking toward her. As they grew closer, Tammy quickened her pace, greeting her mother with open arms and smothering her with a loving embrace. "Hi, Mom, it's so good to see you."

Rose gave her a peck on the cheek. "You too, dear." She turned to her ex- husband and gave him a courteous but friendly hug. "Hello, John," she said, using a dry, flat tone. Clearly sparing no emotion.

"Hello, Rose," John replied, matching her flat tone.

The tension between them was undeniable. Tammy sensed her mother's sadness. Her father chose to be quiet as they walked back to the car, walking two steps behind them while Tammy held her mother's hand and made small talk. Rose made light conversation about the brilliant train ride and the nice weather they were enjoying.

Rose's state of mind improved when she was told they would be having lunch at Maddie's and, as expected, the reunion was bittersweet, continuing where they had left off all those years ago. It seemed time had stood still for the two of them. With so much to say to each other, neither one could speak fast enough.

Tammy's attempts to join in on their witty conversation and

their reminiscing about the good old days had failed miserably. Caught up in the moment of seeing each other again seemed to have made them oblivious to Tammy's presence. She chuckled to herself and opted to take a back seat at one of the barstools, resigned to the fact that it might take the ladies a while to fix lunch.

While the women chatted, Tammy glanced out at the patio and saw her father and uncle had stepped outside, presumably so Uncle Dave could have a cigarette. Aunt Maddie had never smoked and wouldn't allow it in the house. After all the excitement of the morning, the thought of a cigarette appealed to Tammy, so she decided to leave her mother and aunt to their happy reunion and joined the men in the backyard for a smoke before lunch.

After a fulfilling lunch, consisting of roast beef sandwiches and salad, Tammy and her mother decided to take a walk down the road to the local pub. Tammy needed some time alone with her to have a heart-to-heart chat and see where she stood with the move.

Once at the pub, they found a quiet corner booth and sat across from each other. It was still early afternoon so the pub was relatively quiet, which pleased them both given the somber circumstances. Within a few minutes, a young waitress with a blonde ponytail approached their table and took Tammy's order of two glasses of wine.

Rose purposely avoided eye contact with her daughter and stared down at her glass with a forlorn expression while circling the rim with her index finger as she spoke. "So, this time tomorrow, you'll be on an airplane on your way to the States."

"Mom, I know you're not entirely happy about this, but you've also known this is something I've wanted for such a long time." Tammy reached for her mother's hand. "I'm going to miss you so much, and I promise you I'll keep in touch...even though you're afraid I won't," Tammy said, trying to reassure her.

Rose looked up to meet her daughter's eyes and spoke softly. "Tammy, sweetheart, don't get me wrong. I'm really happy for you." She paused, closing her eyes briefly. "It's just so sudden. In the back of my mind, I've always known this day would eventually come, but now that it's here and everything is happening so fast...well, I'm having a hard time dealing with it." Rose swallowed the lump in her throat and quickly continued before Tammy had a chance to respond. "Little by little, I'm losing my family. First your father, then Donna, and now my youngest. Jenny is the only one left. And that's another thing. Jenny is going to be furious when she finds out you left without saying goodbye to her."

"I'll write her a long letter. I promise. I'll make it right, Mom." This wasn't easy, Tammy thought. She hated to see her mother hurting, especially since she was the cause of her pain. Wishing she could make it easier, but not knowing how, frustrated Tammy beyond reason. Squeezing her mother's hand harder, she tried desperately to cheer her up with smiles and by speaking with a more confident and happy tone. Then, suddenly, she remembered her father's promise. "Hey, Dad said he would buy you a plane ticket to come visit me next year. You've never been to the States, Mom. I bet you'll love it!"

Rose huffed at her daughter's comment. "I'm not going to hold my breath, Tammy. Knowing your father, he's just saying that to make me feel better."

Rolling her eyes, Tammy sighed. "Oh, come on, Mom...I'll make sure he sticks to his word." Wanting to sound sincere and convince her mother that everything was going to be okay, Tammy repeated herself. "I promise."

Her mother wasn't buying it and remained stubborn, shaking her head from side to side as she spoke. "Honestly, Tammy, I just don't like the idea of you being so far away. I know you're all grown up now and you've lived on your own for quite some time, but you're still my youngest daughter. You're my baby! I'm sorry, I'm just having a hard time letting you go."

"Mom, I'm going to be living with Dad. Doesn't that make you feel a little better? It's not like I'll be all by myself in some strange country. To be perfectly honest, it's going to feel weird living with a parent again."

"I know. It's just me being me, and I'll deal with it the best I can. I'm not trying to make this harder for you or make you feel worse than you already do, but I'm going to miss you so much when you're gone. I know Donna was much younger when she went to go live with your father and got into all sorts of trouble. I just hope you're more mature and won't make the same mistakes she did." Tears began to roll down Rose's cheeks. "It tears me apart not knowing where she is or what's happened to her. I ask myself every day. Is she still alive? Does she have a home?" Pulling a tissue from her handbag and wiping her eyes, Rose continued to speak between sobs. "Why doesn't she write to any of us to let us know she's okay? Is it because she's dead? I don't know what to think anymore, Tammy, and I'm afraid I may lose you next."

Tammy walked around the table and hugged her mother from behind. She couldn't stand to see her cry. "Oh, Mom, I'm sure she's okay. Whatever reason she has for not contacting us, I'm sure it's a good one. I'm certain we'll hear from her all in good time."

Her mother wiped her eyes again with her now saturated tissue and squeezed her daughter's hand. "I'm sure you're right, dear. It's just the not knowing that's driving me crazy." Attempting to gather her composure, Rose shook her hair and raised her head. She let go of Tammy's hand and dabbed her eyes one last time. "Okay, enough of this talk. Let's enjoy the rest of our visit. My train leaves in a few hours, so I want to make the most of what little time I have left with you."

Tammy admired and appreciated her mother for being strong for her benefit; despite the obvious hurt she was feeling. "Okay,

Mom, you've got it," Tammy said with a smile while picking up the two empty glasses. "Why don't I get us a couple more drinks?"

"That would be nice. Thank you."

The next hour proved to be much better. Finally, Tammy was coming to terms with and feeling more comfortable about leaving her mother. Yes, it was going to be hard, but Tammy promised to shorten the distance between them with as many phone calls and letters as she could.

When the time came to return to the train station, Rose surprisingly managed to keep herself together. Only a few departing tears were shed as Tammy and her mother said their goodbyes. Standing on the platform while waving at the departing train, Tammy knew she and her mother were both going to be okay.

CHAPTER 9

*T*wo months had passed since Tammy left England. Now she was settled and living with her father and stepmother, Joanne, in the small town of Lonesridge, located in Northern California.

Joanne had a feeling she would be returning with John. They had discussed the idea before he left, so it was no surprise to her when he called with his arrival times and casually mentioned that he had a companion with him. She knew right away it was Tammy. Excited to finally be meeting John's youngest daughter, she made every effort to make her feel welcome and at home.

Her father's house was an older two-story, five-bedroom, two-bath home perched high on a hill overlooking Lonesridge. The outside of the home had white siding, black trim, and a large front porch that spanned the full width of the house. Stone steps led up to a heavy wooden front door and pots filled with mums and pink roses were placed sporadically around the porch. Three white ceiling fans spanned the area for hot summer days. A white wicker loveseat and matching chairs with colorful flowery cushions made it an inviting and relaxing place to lounge around and read a good book.

A beautiful rock wall surrounded the grassy lawn in front and continued around to the large back yard. More grass carpeted the garden with surrounding apple, plum, and apricot trees. Blackberries and raspberries made their homes along the back wall.

Originally, the house had had three bedrooms and a bathroom on the ground floor, and three more bedrooms and another bathroom upstairs. John had turned one of the upstairs bedrooms into his office, and Joanne had done the same with one of the bedrooms downstairs. To make the living room bigger, they'd knocked out a wall to one of the other bedrooms, leaving one bedroom and bathroom overlooking the backyard on the ground floor. This was Tammy's room.

As the focal point of the open-plan living room and dining room, an antique cast iron wood stove stood on a stone hearth against the east wall. Both John and Joanne were avid book readers, evident with the floor-to-ceiling bookshelves that lined every room, including the bedrooms. Her father still didn't have a TV, which reminded Tammy of her childhood days. She grew up with her father preferring the company of a good book to watching television. Although, occasionally, he gathered the family around the dining room table to play board games instead.

Tammy and her mother had always welcomed game night. It was a time for bonding and spending quality time with the otherwise busy man of the house. Rose would spend hours in the kitchen preparing a delicious feast while Tammy settled down at the table, eager to learn new board game strategies from her father. Always feeling intimidated by their father's strict working conditions when he was home, Donna and Jenny couldn't warm up to their father so easily. For them, game night was an order by their father, not a choice.

Like her mother, Joanne stayed home and took care of Tammy's new half- brother, Andrew. With the pressures of raising a toddler, Joanne struggled to keep a clean house; dishes were constantly piled in the sink, toys were scattered throughout the house, and dirty clothes were always piled high on the tiled floor of the laundry room.

Because Tammy had entered the States on a visitor's visa, she was unable to work. Being her sponsor, her father had filed papers with the Immigration Department to change her status to a green card within a week of her arrival. Once approved—which could take months if not years—she would finally be able to not only work but also learn to drive. In the meantime, she was happy to help Joanne around the house and watch Andrew when needed.

Being a writer, her father insisted on peace and quiet most of the time. Now with a toddler in the house, that had become impossible, except during nap times. Frustrated, he decided to rent an office above a store in town and was now working outside the home much of the time.

On the increasingly rare occasions he was home, Joanne and Tammy tried their best to keep the house quiet, but they often failed. Like most toddlers, Andrew frequently had temper tantrums. During such incidents, they would first hear the heavy footsteps of her father marching across the office floor above them, and then they'd hear the office door slam and the stomping of his feet down the stairs. In a heated state, he'd give them a snarl followed by a string of grunts and moans as he stormed out of the house, slamming the door behind him.

Once he was out of the house, Tammy and Joanne would simply look at each other, shrug their shoulders, smirk a little bit at his child-like behavior and continue on with their business. To Tammy, this was all too familiar. "Some things just never change," she often chuckled to herself.

Following these incidents, they both knew he would probably spend the night at the office, only to return the next morning, chirpy and happy, acting as if nothing had happened. For Tammy, it was like history repeating itself, but Joanne had learnt to accept his moods and never question them—just like Tammy's mother had done.

Surprisingly, Tammy sometimes found herself homesick for England. She missed her friends, her independence, and even her ex-boyfriend. With nothing exciting to report, she hadn't kept her promise to write to her friends. Because she couldn't work or drive, she hadn't been anywhere or met anyone new. Although it saddened her to say it, her life had become boring. It was nothing like she had imagined or hoped for, and she was feeling somewhat disappointed. The truth was, she had no friends, no social life, no boyfriend, and her sex life had been non-existent since her arrival.

The hunt for Donna was at a dead end with nothing to go on. She had made inquiry phone calls to the children's home and to the detective in charge of the case, but they weren't able to tell her anything she didn't already know. They were waiting for some kind of lead to pop up, but so far, nothing had. Tammy asked if there was anything she should be doing, but the police said they'd already done everything possible. Despite photos being strung throughout the Boston area and the staff and older children from the home having been interviewed extensively, no one seemed to know anything. Now all they could do was wait.

She wrote only to her mother and Jenny, but lied by telling them she was happy and loving her new life in the States. Her relationship with Jenny had become strained since she left without saying goodbye. Tammy tried to make amends with a long letter filled with numerous apologies, but Jenny never acknowledged them or officially accepted her apology. In the time she had been in the States, she had only received one letter from her, and that was just to say how disappointed she was that Tammy had upped and left without a word. She understood Jenny's anger and blamed only herself.

Tammy found adjusting to living back with parents beyond difficult. After living on her own, she now had to live by their rules and respect the eleven o'clock curfew they had given her. So, especially without a car, she was limited on where she could go.

Being a small town, Lonesridge had no bus or taxi service, but Main Street was within walking distance of the house. As the core of the town, with a variety of restaurants and shops, it was here where she spent many afternoons strolling and browsing. Her favorite place to go was the small park at the top of Main Street. An area of shade trees and green grass scattered with wooden park benches and picnic tables. It was a place visited by daily shoppers taking a rest, children playing on the grass, and proud dog owners walking their pets. On the days Joanne didn't need Tammy's help, she often spent time alone at the park under a shade tree with a good book.

While spending one such afternoon at the park engrossed in her latest read, she lost track of time. Glancing down at her watch, she saw it was almost dinner time. Knowing Joanne would be needing her help, she gathered up her things and headed home.

Upon entering the house, the essence of a home-cooked meal filled the air. Damn, what smells so good? Tammy thought while drawing more of the aroma through her nose.

After setting down her bag in the most convenient place, which happened to be the couch, she made her way toward the already set dining room table where she noticed another plate had been added. She smiled down at her little brother and watched him playing contently with his wooden blocks in the playpen.

She heard Joanne in the kitchen, who obviously hadn't realized Tammy was home, and called in her direction. "Hi, Joanne, I'm home. Do you need help with anything?"

Amongst the clatter of dishes, she heard Joanne reply, "Hi, Tammy, no thanks. I think I have it under control. We're having meatloaf for dinner. Just keep an eye on Andrew for me, if you wouldn't mind?"

"Sure, no problem." Tammy bent down and gathered Andrew in her arms; he was still amused by the one block he was holding.

Tammy took a seat at the table and bounced him on her knees while he continued to play.

"I see there's another place set for dinner. Are we having company?" Tammy asked.

"Yes, Raymond is joining us," Joanne replied as she came out of the kitchen, wiping her hands with a dish towel and taking a seat at the table across from her.

"Who's he?"

"Oh, he's a good friend of your father. He owns the contracting company that did the renovations on this house."

"What about his wife? Won't she be coming?"

Joanne shook her head and chuckled. "Oh, Raymond isn't the marrying kind. He's a few years younger than your dad, but he has no kids and has never been married. In my opinion, I don't think he ever will. He likes to play around too much." She then added in a whisper, "Between you and me, he seems to have a different woman every month. Although him and your dad are very good friends; his personal life is really none of our business."

Amused by her comments, Tammy laughed. "Ahh, I see. What time is he coming over?" Tammy asked while putting Andrew back in his playpen.

Joanne glanced down at her watch. "In about an hour. Which gives me just enough time to shower and freshen up before he arrives." She quickly stood up and removed her apron. "Mind if I leave you in charge of Andrew? Maybe you can take him out in the backyard for a while and let him play outside before dinner?"

"Of course. Go take your shower." As Joanne headed upstairs, Tammy turned to her little brother. "Come on, big fella. Let's go play outside," she cooed, heading out the back door.

While watching Andrew play in the green turtle sandbox, Tammy hadn't heard her father come home. Startled by his presence at the back door, she jerked her head in surprise when he called out across the yard.

"Hi, Tammy, where's Joanne?"

"Hi, Dad, I didn't hear you come in. She's upstairs taking a shower."

"Oh, okay. I'm off to take one too. Can you listen for the front door? Raymond is coming for dinner tonight."

"Yes, I know. Joanne already told me. I'll take Andrew indoors so I can hear him knock. He's beginning to get bored with the sand- box anyway."

"Thanks. I won't be long."

Tammy picked up Andrew, brushed the sand off his clothes, and headed for the living room. He smiled and made a chorus of loud baby noises as she placed him down on a blanket in the middle of the room and showered him with wooden blocks and colorful books. Feeling content, she watched him happily while she waited for their guest to arrive.

CHAPTER 10

Fifteen minutes later, there was a knock at the front door. Keeping an eye on her brother, Tammy left him to play while she answered it. When she opened the door, she froze. Time stood still. Subconsciously, her jaw dropped. Before her stood an extremely handsome man holding a bottle of red wine. This was Raymond? Dad's friend? Was her first thought.

He was tall with short brown hair, a broad, dark mustache, and high cheekbones that looked chiseled into his somewhat chubby cheeks, which had a slight distinction of redness to them—in an attractive way. Tammy wasn't sure if he was cold or just blushing, but as she stood in the doorway staring at him, Tom Selleck came to mind. She lost herself in his deep blue eyes, framed by long, thick black eyelashes. When he flashed a heart-warming smile, she found herself being drawn in even more. He wore blue jeans, blue loafers, and a blue and white checked shirt with the top buttons undone, revealing a few dark chest hairs.

Joanne had told her that he was just a few years younger than her father, but he seemed a lot younger. She could feel her heart rate increasing and soon realized she'd been staring at him in silence with her mouth drooped open like a puppy dog.

He spoke softly, albeit with a hint of nervousness, in a manly, alluring voice. "Er, hi. Is John home? You must be his daughter. Tammy, right?"

"Oh, yes. I'm so sorry. Hello," she said, feeling utterly stupid and embarrassed for gawking at him. She pushed the door open with the back of her body and motioned him inside with her hand. "Come on in. My dad and Joanne will be down shortly." She led him toward the couch. "Please have a seat on the settee. I'm just watching Andrew for a moment."

As he walked by her, she couldn't help noticing the pleasant scent of masculine cologne trailing behind him like an invisible shadow. Tammy's eyes continued to follow him as he took a seat on the brown leather couch. After making himself comfortable, Tammy saw he was still holding the bottle of wine. "Here, let me take that from you," she said while reaching for the bottle.

"Thanks," he said as he handed it to her. His friendly smile and perfect white teeth warmed her. Casually, she walked over to the dining room table and set the bottle down.

Since arriving home from the park, Tammy hadn't had a chance to freshen up or change. She felt under-dressed in her blue jeans, black cowboy boots, red t-shirt, and minimal makeup. Feeling nervous, she avoided eye contact with Raymond and took a seat in the armchair across the room next to Andrew, who was still happily playing on the blanket. With a moment of uncomfortable silence, Tammy took the edge off by twiddling her fingers and directing her attention to her little brother. Finally, Raymond broke the silence.

"So, how do you like living here in the States?"

Trying to act normal and not let her racing heart control her, Tammy forced a calm voice. "I love it. It's a lot different from England though, and I'm still trying to get used to all the changes."

Raymond gave her another one of his warm smiles. "I'm sure

it's quite a change. I spoke to John a few weeks ago. He mentioned you were here but, of course, being your dad, he didn't tell me how pretty you were."

Surprise by his comment, Tammy brushed it off as him merely trying to be polite and thanked him with a subtle shy smile.

He continued to compliment her. "I love your red hair. We don't see too many redheads over here." Feeling more at ease, Raymond leaned back in his seat, rested his elbows on the arms of the chair and smiled. "And that English accent of yours is mighty fine too, if you don't mind me saying."

Feeling herself blush, Tammy lowered her head and thanked him again. Uncomfortable with his praises, she needed an excuse to leave the room so she could compose herself. Secretly, she was wishing her father and Joanne would just hurry up. Using Andrew for an excuse, she quickly leaned over and picked him up. "Will you excuse me for a minute? I need to wash this little boy's hands and face before dinner."

"Sure, no problem."

But, before Tammy had a chance to leave the room, Raymond stood and walked over to her. She watched as he put his hand out to Andrew nestled in her arms. He and Tammy chuckled when Andrew grasped one of Raymond's fingers with his tiny hand and gave them both a goofy grin.

"He's growing so fast. Hey there, buddy. How are you doing?" Raymond said in a playful voice while Andrew continued to pull on his finger.

Tammy hadn't expected him to approach her. His masculine hands caught her attention as he played with Andrew. Again, she smelled his cologne and took a deep breath, inhaling the delicious scent. Strangely stirred by his presence, she began to back away. "Er, will you excuse me? I won't be long." And, without looking back, she hastily left the room, leaving Raymond by himself.

Relieved to be out the room, Tammy needed some time to pull herself together and calm her pounding heart. She argued with herself about how absurd it was to be attracted to a man twice her age, especially one that was a dear friend of her father.

With haste, she closed the bathroom door behind her and sat Andrew down on the closed toilet seat before grabbing a soaked wash- cloth and began to wash his face. Andrew tried his best to pull away and fuss. "Hush, little guy. I'm almost done," she said as she battled with him to open his hands. While uncurling and wiping down each of Andrew's tiny fingers one by one, Tammy tried to think of a logical reason why she was feeling flustered around her father's friend, but couldn't explain any of it and refused to accept the fact that she might be attracted to him.

A few minutes later, she heard voices coming from the living room. "Thank God," she whispered out loud, releasing a sigh of relief. Dad and Joanne must have finally come downstairs. Picking up Andrew, Tammy took a deep breath and returned to the living room.

Joanne looked attractive in her black slacks and red turtleneck sweater. She had let her long black hair flow freely down her back, which she seldom did, and she had applied some light makeup, which was another rarity. She was standing in the middle of the room talking to Raymond, while her father, who looked comfortable in his tan slacks and beige sweater, poured wine at the table.

Joanne and Raymond ended their conversation and glanced over at Tammy when she entered the room.

"There you are," Joanne said while walking toward her and taking Andrew in her arms.

"Sorry, I was just giving Andrew a wash before dinner."

"Raymond tells me you've already met," Joanne said as she nestled Andrew in her arm.

"Yes, we have," Tammy, replied, giving Raymond a courteous smile.

Joanne glanced over at John, who was still at the table. "Well, it looks like your father has poured the wine. Why don't I go serve up dinner so we can eat?" she said with a satisfied smile. She then proceeded to walk toward the table, where she strapped Andrew into his high chair and disappeared into the kitchen. Raymond took a seat across from John. Within a few minutes, they were sipping on their drinks and engaged in a deep conversation over John's latest book.

The sun was beginning to set outside, and a slight breeze caused the lace curtain to flap like a sail. Irritated by the noise, Tammy walked over and closed the window.

Happy to see her father had poured her a glass of wine, she reached over and took a huge gulp to help calm her nerves. Pausing their conversation for a moment, her father and Raymond watched with amazement as Tammy downed her drink with a single swig before setting the glass back down on the table. With a smirk, she glanced over at Raymond. "Good wine," she said. And quickly added, "Well, I'm going to go help Joanne in the kitchen." Giving neither of the men a chance to speak, she quickly vacated the table.

With the aroma of meatloaf invading the air and dinner served, Joanne took a seat next to Andrew's high chair so she could feed him while Tammy sat across from Raymond, next to her father. Enjoying how the wine was soothing her, Tammy reached over and poured herself another glass.

The strong friendship between her father and Raymond was clearly noticeable during dinner. Throughout the meal, they talked and laughed about various topics. John had some questions about the house, and Raymond wanted to hear all about his books and what was next.

Having been quiet throughout the entire meal—mainly to let her father and Raymond catch up—Tammy was uncertain what to say when Raymond directed a question at her. "So, Tammy, what are your plans now that you're here?"

With no hesitation, her father quickly answered for her. "Well, I'm hoping she goes to college and gets a degree behind her," John said, glaring intensely at his daughter.

Tammy turned toward her father, giving him an evil but playful stare. "I just got here, Dad. There's plenty of time for me to go to college. Right now, you're teaching me to drive and I'm busy helping Joanne with Andrew. Once I have my driver's license then I'll look in to college."

With a puzzled look, Raymond asked Tammy another question. "How old are you?"

Tammy took a sip of wine. "I just turned eighteen not so long ago."

"But you're drinking alcohol," Raymond stated, still looking puzzled .

"I've been drinking since I was sixteen. It's so different over here. In this country, I can only drink at my dad's house. In England, you can drink beer or wine with a meal at sixteen in a restaurant, so long, as it is ordered, by an adult. You can legally drink in a bar when you turn eighteen. I've been drinking in bars since I was seventeen and never been asked for my ID. But, over here, I just don't get it. You're legally an adult at eighteen, you can marry, become a parent, go off to war and fight for your country, but you can't celebrate any of those accomplishments with a drink because the drinking age over here is twenty-one. It makes no sense to me."

Both John and Raymond nodded. "Makes no sense to me either," her father replied.

"Well, have you seen much since you've been here? Have you been to the small Gold Rush town?" Raymond asked. "That's not its real name by the way, but it's what we all call it around here."

"Er, no, I haven't seen much yet. Dad is busy working and Joanne has Andrew. I plan on doing some sightseeing once I'm able to drive."

"Well, I can take you to the old gold mining town tomorrow if you'd like? It's only three miles away." Raymond paused and looked over at John. "If that's okay with you, John? You're a busy guy, so I'd be happy to show Tammy around."

Tammy didn't know what to say. Shocked that he may be asking her out on a date, she waited to reply, wondering if her father was going to speak for her again.

Not having an immediate answer, her father turned to Joanne for some insight. A simple shrug of her shoulders suggested she wasn't going to offer any help on the matter, so John opted to put her on the spot. "Well, Joanne, what do you think? It's really up to you. Do you need help with anything tomorrow?"

Joanne narrowed her eyes at her husband. She didn't like the decision being left up to her and hesitated before answering. "Er, no, I should be fine if she wants to go." She turned to Tammy. "Do you want to go?"

Well, this is awkward, Tammy thought to herself. Of course she wanted to go. It would be nice to do something different for a change, but she still wasn't sure if it was such a good idea.

Since Raymond's arrival, her head had been in an all-out tailspin. She didn't know what to do. What if she was attracted to him? How uncomfortable would it be if she decided to go? She thought for a moment and concluded that whatever she was or wasn't feeling didn't matter; Raymond would never be interested in her anyway. She was twenty years younger than him and she was his friend's daughter, so she figured it would be okay. Feeling a little tipsy from the wine, she gave Raymond a smile. "Yes, I would love to go. I think it will be fun."

"That's great! What time shall I pick you up?" Raymond cheered with excitement lingering in his voice.

Tammy took another sip of wine. "How about eleven? That'll give me enough time to help Joanne with breakfast and get myself ready."

"Sounds good. I'll be here at eleven."

Tammy gave him another smile and stood up, pushing her chair away with the backs of her knees. "Great. Well, if you'll all excuse me, I'm going to go on the front porch for a cigarette."

A look of surprise blanketed Raymond's face. "You smoke?"

With a contented grin, he added, "So do I. Mind if I join you? I've never liked being the only smoker at the dinner table." With an affirmative smile from Tammy, he excused himself from the table and followed her out the front door.

It was a cool, refreshing evening with just a slight chill in the air, and hundreds of twinkling stars lit up the dark, moonless sky. The wind had finally died down, the air was still, and the trees rose like soldiers standing to attention across the horizon. Tammy took a seat on one of the wicker chairs, lit her cigarette, and took a long, much-needed drag. The smoke rushing down to her lungs instantly satisfied the deep craving she'd had for some time and delivered a sense of calmness throughout her entire body. Never could she imagine quitting. What else could be more satisfying?

Raymond remained standing with his back to her, looking up at the skies from the porch. With one hand nestled in his front jean pocket, he looked like a natural smoker. "What a beautiful night this is. It's so peaceful. I don't even hear the crickets," he said, exhaling smoke and turning around to face her. Saying nothing, he stood motionless and stared at Tammy, taking deep hits on his cigarette.

Tammy looked up and stared back. After a few minutes of uncomfortable silence, she finally asked him. "What? What are you looking at?"

Raymond let out a small laugh and looked her straight in the eyes. Leaning back against the pillar of the porch and folding his arms across his chest, he spoke with a grin. "You're going to do well over here. You're different and you stand out. You really are quite striking."

"Striking? What are you talking about? You're being silly," Tammy remarked, trying to brush off the fact that he might be flirting with her.

"It's that red hair of yours and your fair complexion and freckles. And oh, that English accent, I could listen to it all day," Raymond confessed.

"That's bloody rubbish. After a while, people will get used to it."

"Nah, not here. I think you must be the only English girl in town. Trust me, all Americans love the English accent."

Meanwhile, back in the house, her parents were having their own discussion at the table.

"So are you okay with Tammy going with Raymond tomorrow?" Joanne asked John while rocking Andrew to sleep in her lap.

John sat across from her, looking down at his glass of wine as he curled his fingers in a circular motion around the stem. He looked a little concerned but tried not to show it when he answered. "Sure, why not? I'm sure it'll be fine. Raymond is only trying to help. He knows neither one of us have time to play tour guide with her."

Joanne knew he wasn't being entirely honest with her or himself. Surely he must have some concerns. "Are you sure about that? You know how he is with the ladies."

Irritated by her remark, he replied with a sharper tone. "Oh, come on. I don't think he'll try and hit on my daughter for Christ's sake. He's twice her age. Will you quit worrying so much?"

To help calm him down, Joanne softened her voice. "I'm not worried, John. I'm just a little concerned. But if you think it's okay, then I do too."

Before John could say any more, Raymond and Tammy returned from outside. John didn't want to admit it, but the luring smile Raymond gave his daughter as he closed the door behind them made him quite uncomfortable.

"Brrr, it's getting rather chilly out there," Tammy said, blowing into her cupped hands and rubbing them together.

Raymond looked down at his watch and then over at Joanne and John at the table. "Well, it's getting late. I guess I should get going." He turned to Tammy. "So, I'll pick you up around eleven?"

"Sounds good. And, thank you, I'm looking forward to it," Tammy answered as she sat back down at the table to finish her wine. John got up and walked Raymond out while Joanne went upstairs to put Andrew to sleep.

As Tammy sat at the table alone, thoughts of what she should wear tomorrow entered her head. But what was she thinking? This wasn't a date. This was just a friend of her father's showing her the town. She stood up, shook her head, and laughed at herself and her thoughts as she began to clear the table.

After Tammy had washed the dishes, she spent the rest of the night playing scrabble with Joanne. John retired to his office. Nothing more was mentioned about her day tomorrow with Raymond, but the questions and confusion constantly whirled around Tammy's mind.

CHAPTER 11

*W*ith the anticipation of spending the next day with Raymond, Tammy had a sleepless night of staring at the ceiling from her bed. She wanted to break away from what reminded her of a high school crush, telling herself repeatedly that tomorrow she must act mature, stay calm, and not make a fool of herself. She couldn't let Raymond know about the absurd feelings she was having toward him.

Tammy woke the next morning feeling fatigued because of her lack of sleep. She glanced over at the clock and saw it was already after eight. She sat up when she heard the clanging of dishes coming from the kitchen. After rubbing her eyes, she swung her legs out of bed, stretched, and stood up. She reached for her light blue housecoat hanging on the closet door, wrapped herself in it, and headed for the kitchen.

Joanne was now sitting at the table in her red bathrobe with her hair tied back into a ponytail. Andrew sat in his high chair next to her, wriggling with excitement from head to toe every time she fed him a spoonful of oatmeal.

"Morning, Joanne, want some coffee?" Tammy asked, followed by a yawn.

"Sounds great. I've already made a pot," she said while coaxing another spoonful of oatmeal into Andrew's mouth.

Tammy disappeared into the kitchen for a few minutes. With two mugs of hot coffee in hand, she reappeared at the table and placed the mugs in front of them. Tammy wrapped her hands around the warm cup and took a sip. The hot liquid felt good against the back of her throat. She thought the first cup of the day always tasted the best. "Where's Dad?" she asked in between sips.

"He already left for the office. I guess he wanted to get an early start. Looks like it's going to be just me and the little guy today since you're going sight-seeing with Raymond."

Tammy took another sip of coffee, savoring the flavor before answering. "It was really nice of him to offer to take me. I'm really looking forward to it."

Joanne tried not to show her concerns. "Yes, it was," she agreed. "I'm sure you'll have a great time," she added, wiping Andrew's mouth.

"Thanks. After my coffee, I'll take a shower...unless you need help with anything?"

"No, I'm fine, you go ahead. I can put Andrew in the playpen while I get dressed."

After her shower, Tammy faced the dreaded task of figuring out what to wear. She wanted to grasp his attention and look attractive yet not reveal too much or dress too skimpy. She'd heard on the radio it was going to be a warm day of above-average temperatures in the seventies, with blue skies and no wind. For October, that was good.

After some major deliberating, she finally decided on wearing a blue denim mini-skirt, brown cowboy boots, and a light blue tank top that showed off just a hint of cleavage. She would bring her short denim jacket for later in the day. Her makeup was light but just enough to accentuate her high cheekbones and green eyes. She

took a quick glance in the full-size mirror; happy with her appearance, she smiled at herself, tossed her hair back with a flirty swing,
and glanced down at her watch. It was ten thirty. He would be here
soon, she thought with excitement. Nervous with the anticipation
of his arrival, she had just enough time to step out on the front
porch and smoke a cigarette to calm her nerves.

The cool, brisk air felt good against her skin, and the sun glistened through the trees against a backdrop of cloudless, bright
blue skies.

She had been sitting contently for a few minutes enjoying her
cigarette, feeling more relaxed, when she noticed a silver metallic
Ford Pick-up truck pull up in front of the house and park. After
the driver door swung open, Raymond stepped out. While the
shadows of the porch were hiding her from Raymond's view, she
could already see him clearly. She liked what she saw. She couldn't
deny it. He looked sexy, wearing dark shades and jingling his truck
keys in his hand as he walked toward the house. His faded blue
jeans fit his body like a glove, accentuating every curve in his
muscular, toned legs. His gold- tone belt buckle glistened in the
sun, and his long-sleeve denim shirt, with the sleeves rolled up
mid-way, was tucked loosely into his jeans. Beneath his jeans, the
toes and heels of cowboy boots peeked out.

As he approached the front gate, she stood and walked over to
the top of the steps. She took a long hit of her cigarette and
exhaled a hurried cloud of hazy blue smoke. "Hi. You're early," she
said with a soft, alluring smile.

He paused at the bottom of the steps and looked up in her
direction. He removed his sunglasses slowly and smiled. Stunned
by her appearance, he ignored her comment. "Wow! Don't you
look nice? May I join you?" he asked jokingly.

"Sure, like I said, you're early."

"Well, I just couldn't wait to see you again," he teased as he
quickly strode up the steps to join her.

When he reached the porch, he stood close to her. He was tall, over six feet, and that familiar cologne wafted through the air to greet her yet again. It was the same as the one he had worn the night before. Without saying a word, he reached into his shirt pocket, pulled out a pack of Marlboro Reds cigarettes and lit one.

They both began to breathe a little heavier as they stood staring at each other in silence. The strong attraction was palpable, but neither one wanted to admit it. At that precise moment, Tammy wanted him to take her in his arms and kiss her passionately. Instead, he guided her back to reality. "Well, are you ready to go?" he said hastily, trying to brush aside the unforgivable thoughts he was having.

Tammy quickly shrugged off her fantasy. "Yes, I am. I just need to grab my purse," she replied before stubbing out her cigarette in a nearby ashtray and turning toward the front door.

"I'll wait right here," Raymond said with a grin.

Tammy felt herself being drawn into him by his gorgeous smile. Anxiously, she opened the door, rushed inside, and leaned against the cool wood of the now closed door. She inhaled a long, hard breath, causing her to tremble as air rushed deep into her lungs. Pull yourself together, Tammy, jeez, she snapped at herself. Almost forgetting what she came in for, she headed toward her bedroom and grabbed her brown purse from the bottom of the bed. Happy that Joanne had already gone upstairs, she hollered up from the bottom of the stairway.

"Joanne, I'm leaving now. I'll see you later."

"Okay. Have fun!" was the faint reply from upstairs.

"I will!" Tammy shouted as she went back outside onto the porch.

Raymond stood up from the wicker chair where he had been sitting. "Ready?" he asked.

"I am," she replied, skipping down the steps toward his truck.

Once Raymond fired up the engine, the radio instantly came to life playing Kenny Rodgers, *The Gambler*. Tammy found herself liking the western cowboy lifestyle in this part of the States. She enjoyed listening to the country music and loved how everyone dressed in jeans and cowboy boots and hats. It seemed much more laid back than the disco music, glitter, and big hair found back in England.

They took Route 49 north and headed toward the Gold Rush town. It was a beautiful scenic drive through the country. The road was narrow and windy, hugging the twists and turns of the hilly countryside. Blackberries, which were succulent and ripe this time of year, grew in masses along both sides of the road. It was October, early fall, and many trees had already lost their leaves, but there were still a few that had glorious shades of reds and yellows that glistened in the sun.

During the ten-minute drive to their destination, Raymond filled her in with some history of the town. He explained how it was a gold rush town in the 1850s and was now a State preserved historical park and a National Historical Landmark. Tammy was fascinated by the history and couldn't wait to see it for herself.

They parked in a lot behind Main Street, since no driving was allowed beyond that point. After Raymond locked the truck and stuffed the keys in his front pocket, they casually strolled side by side toward Main Street.

Tammy stood and stared down at the small town. She could see to the end of the road, about a half-mile away. It was like stepping back in time into an old western movie. All the buildings were made of red brick or logs, and each had a wooden porch and benches in front for shaded resting spots. Handmade store signs hung from chains; she imagined them swaying noisily in the breeze on a windy day. Chalkboards stood in front of many stores, promoting the daily specials, and thanks to the main road being made up mainly of dirt, clouds of dust kicked up into the air with each step as Tammy and Raymond walked along together.

A finely polished, red and gold antique fire truck from the 1850s sat at the top of the street with a golden plaque describing the town's history displayed in front. Tourists were scattered throughout the area, popping in and out of stores and clicking their cameras at the various sights.

While walking through the town, Tammy noticed two hotels and several saloons with squeaky saloon-style doors. A variety of eateries from ice cream parlors, coffee and pastry stores to fancy sit-down restaurants lined the street, along with a selection of gift stores. During their walk, they watched hard candy being made and a blacksmith making horseshoes. They bought homemade jellies and jams for Joanne, and Raymond bought Tammy some homemade scented candles.

Tammy was having a wonderful time, but no matter how she looked at her day with Raymond, she felt like she was on her first date. She found him easy to talk to and there was never a moment of silence between them. He walked her through all the stores, excitedly pointing out all the historical artifacts and photos.

Tammy loved how all the merchants wore 1850s-style costumes. The women wore long dresses and white aprons with their hair pinned up in a simple bun. The men wore long overcoats and pants, white shirts, black neckties and cowboy hats. There was even a place where you could have your picture taken while dressed in costume.

As soon as Raymond saw the sign, he said, "Let's have our picture taken, it'll be fun!"

She looked up at the sign and read it out loud. "Twentieth-century photos taken in nineteenth-century costumes." Tammy agreed it would be fun and so they both entered the store, laughing like over-excited children about to have their photo taken in Santa's grotto.

The walls inside were decorated with seductive red and gold wallpaper. Photos of previous tourists dressed in costume hung in rows. A tall blond skinny man, also dressed in costume, appeared and raised his hat to them as he welcomed them to his establishment. After giving them a tour, he showed them a rack of costumes they could choose from for their picture. After at least twenty minutes of giggling and joking around, they both decided what outfit they wanted to wear and left to go change.

Raymond came out first, wearing a black tailcoat, black pants, a white shirt with a black neck tie, a black top hat, and a black cane swinging from his right hand.

A few minutes later, Tammy appeared from behind the purple curtain of her dressing room, wearing a floor-length light blue dress with long sleeves, ballooned shoulders, and a large blue bow tied in the back. The collar was high and trimmed with white lace. Delicate white-lace shoes and a white-lace umbrella completed her attire.

Feeling the effects of his costume, Raymond decided to do a little role-playing. He rose from his seat, removed his hat, and bowed to her.

"Well, hello, my lady."

Tammy giggled and gave him a slight curtsy. "Good day, sir," she said, flaunting her best impersonation of the Queen's English.

The storeowner suddenly reappeared, interrupting their fun, and asked if they were ready to have their picture taken.

With a nod, Raymond gestured his arm to Tammy. She happily accepted and hooked arms with him as they followed the merchant to the camera. When they posed for their picture. The photographer had Tammy sit on a chair with the closed umbrella held in both hands upside down in front of her. He then had Raymond stand behind her, slightly to her left, with one hand on her shoulder. As soon as Raymond touched her, he gave her shoulder a slight squeeze, which sent a flutter of shivers down her spine.

They ordered two sets of prints and laughed hysterically when the storeowner handed them over. Once back in their normal clothes, they walked outside to have a cigarette. Tammy walked to the side of the building and leaned her back against the wall. With one knee bent, she placed the sole of her foot on the wall for support and closed her eyes.

After a few moments, she felt Raymond's warm breath on her face. She slowly opened her eyes and almost froze when she found his face within inches of hers. He leaned into her and rested the palm of his hand on the wall above her left shoulder. "God," he said, "I could get into some serious trouble with you."

Before she could answer, he was kissing her. His kiss was hard and passionate as his weight pushed her back against the wall. Tammy didn't resist. Instead, she moved away from the wall and wrapped both her arms around his neck, pulling him in closer, kissing him with the same passion. Raymond leaned into her body and pressed his muscular chest against hers while snaking his fingers around her narrow waist, deepening his lustful kiss.

Suddenly, he pulled back. Breathing heavily, he managed to say, "Let's get out of here." Not waiting for a reply, he grabbed Tammy's hand. "Come on!" he yelled as he began to run, pulling her behind him.

In a state of confusion and running at an uncomfortable pace that her feet couldn't keep up with, Tammy asked, "Where are we going?"

"I don't know, Tammy. But this isn't good!" He was yelling and sprinting through the town, clearly in a state of panic. Tammy, almost choking on the dust kicked up by Raymond's speeding boots in front of her, was left with no choice but to follow.

CHAPTER 12

*W*hen they finally reached the truck, Tammy all but collapsed against the passenger door, desperately trying to catch her breath. Confused by what had just happened, she waited for Raymond to unlock the truck. Momentarily, she heard the lock release and turned around to open the door.

"Hurry up! Get in!" he hollered from inside the truck.

Raymond was already in the front seat. He didn't look at her; it seemed he couldn't look at her. "What have I done? This is so wrong. What was I thinking?" he mumbled to himself while hunched over the steering wheel. Feeling the anger boiling up in the pit of his stomach, he grabbed the wheel with both hands and squeezed it hard, causing his knuckles to turn white. He could feel the beads of sweat forming on his brow. He wanted to leave. Now. He needed to get away. "Hurry up, Tammy!" he yelled again.

"Okay! Okay!" She yelled back, grabbing the handle and yanking the door open.

Once in the truck, Raymond said nothing. Looking straight ahead, he turned the key, hit the gas, and skidded out onto the main road. Tammy cowered on her side of the bench seat, afraid to speak, feeling confused by his actions and unable to fathom why he was so upset. He continued to drive in silence, only staring at the road ahead. Moments later, he pulled off to the side of the road under a large oak tree and turned off the truck.

An uncomfortable silence followed. Raymond reached for his cigarettes sitting on the dash and fumbled to get one out of the pack. With shaking hands, he managed to lift one up to his mouth and light it. He leaned back in the seat, closed his eyes, and inhaled deeply on the cigarette. Tammy remained motionless and silent, still afraid to move or speak.

Raymond finished his smoke in a matter of minutes, stubbing it out viscously in the ashtray before running his hands through his hair and pulling at it with his fingers. Still grasping his hair, he lowered his forehead onto the steering wheel and looked down at his lap.

"Whatever happened back there; never happened! Do you understand me?" he ordered in a cruel and angry tone.

Tammy could feel tears forming. Not wanting to cry in front of him, she swallowed hard to push them back. She still didn't understand why he was so angry and upset. "What do you mean?" she asked, still struggling to keep back the tears.

He turned his head toward her and glared at her with dark, narrow eyes. "I MEAN it NEVER happened...and you will tell NO ONE about this. Do I make myself clear?"

Tammy spoke softly, trying to calm him. "We only kissed Raymond. It was no big deal. Will you please just calm down?"

"What? Yes, it actually was a big deal, Tammy! I have no idea what I was thinking. You are my friend's daughter, for God's sake! I'm old enough to be your father. Christ! What the fuck was I thinking?" Still shocked, he raised his hands. "What would John think? This is insane. I can't do this. Can you imagine how your father would feel if he found out?"

Unable to hold back the tears anymore, Tammy felt a warm trickle down her cheeks as she tried to reason with him. "I don't understand why you are making such a big deal out of this. We like each other, don't we?" She wiped away her tears. "And as far as my dad is concerned, we don't have to tell him." She paused. "Not yet anyway."

"We can *never* tell him, Tammy! Don't you understand? It would destroy our friendship. I can't even begin to imagine the anger he would feel toward me. No, I'm not willing to take that risk, regardless of how much I'm attracted to you."

In her heart, she knew he was right; her father would never accept it. Not only would Raymond be jeopardizing their friendship, she also risked her father disowning her. Devastated by what was suddenly at stake, her tears began to flow heavier.

To comfort her, Raymond placed his hand on her shoulder, giving it a slight squeeze as he spoke in a softer tone. "Come on, stop crying. I'm sorry I got angry. I'm not angry with you. Just myself for allowing this to happen."

Even though she knew the risks, she refused to give up. With her eyes now swollen and red from her tears, Tammy looked up at him. "I'm as surprised as you are about what happened back there, but I felt the chemistry between us when we kissed. I know you did too. You can't ignore something like that and just pretend it never happened."

Raymond wrapped an arm around her shoulder, hugging her tightly. "Oh, Tammy, I'm flattered that a girl of your age finds me attractive and wants to be with me. You're young, beautiful, and vibrant. Why on earth do you want to be with an old guy like me?"

She smiled and placed her hand on his knee. "Because you're a real man and I feel safe with you. The guys I dated in England were just boys, young, immature, and stupid."

He laughed at her remark, still hugging her while he spoke. "As much as I like you, I can't hurt your father. He would never forgive me for dating his daughter."

"Yes, I know, but can I ask you something?"

"Sure."

"Did you think this would happen? I mean, if you're attracted to me but have no intentions of us dating, why did you invite me here in the first place? I'm sorry, but today has felt like a first date to me. Especially when we kissed."

"I have to admit that yes, I was attracted to you, even before I knew your age. But I thought I had it under control. I invited you with the intentions of just having some fun and making a new friend. I didn't expect it to go this far. You're right, though, there is chemistry between us. I felt it back there too. It consumed me, but I have to fight it and resist the temptations I'm feeling because...because of your father."

Tammy released herself from his hold and reached for her handbag by her feet. She pulled out a pack of cigarettes, took one from the pack and lit it. Leaning back in her seat, she looked over at him with sullen eyes while she smoked.

Thoughts entered her mind. What she felt back there was electrifying. Refusing to let go of something so real and so strong before it had a chance to blossom, Tammy decided to play along but with ulterior motives. "I promise not to say anything. I understand, and like you said, it never happened. Let's just forget it," she said in her sweetest voice.

"Tammy, this isn't easy for me. When I'm with you, you make me feel young and full of life. It's like I'm living my youth again. I've never felt that before with anyone. Then again, I've never dated any one as young as you and to be honest, it scares the hell out of me... and so does your father."

Knowing he was unaware that his hand was now on her knee while he spoke, Tammy stubbed out her unfinished cigarette in the ashtray and reached for his hand. Caressing it softly, she raised it to her mouth and kissed each finger one by one. He didn't pull away. She shifted her body closer to him, placed his hand over her breast, and gave it a gentle squeeze.

Raymond followed her hand with his eyes, admiring her cleavage, feeling her heart beating rapidly beneath his hand. With light fingers and a feathered touch, he began to massage her breast in a slow circular motion. Aroused by his touch, Tammy inhaled a sharp breath and closed her eyes before arching her back and pushing her body closer to him.

Raymond knew this was wrong for so many reasons, but he could no longer resist. Surrendering to his unforgivable desires, he pulled her toward him with force and kissed her with greater passion than before. Tammy welcomed him and matched his passion with a burning hunger and desire of her own. They both needed to stop for air, but neither could let go. There was no going back now. Unable to control himself, he reached up under her tank top and fondled her breasts, squeezing her nipples with his fingertips. He felt the delicate skin harden under his touch as she moaned with pleasure.

While still locked in a kiss, she slid over to his side of the seat and straddled him. Raising her mini skirt to the tops of her thighs, she locked her arms around his neck and pushed his head farther back into the seat. She felt the hard skin of his hands grazing over her legs and up under her skirt. His touch wasn't gentle. The touch of a man, she thought. Filled with lust, he clamped his fingers around the muscle of her buttocks and nuzzled his head between her breasts. Tammy gasped. With one swift move, she peeled her top up over her head and threw it to the passenger side. Now faced with her naked chest, Raymond devoured her, tantalizing each of her nipples with his tongue before engulfing them with his mouth. His hunger for her had overtaken his senses and he was fast losing control.

Feeling the same hunger, Tammy lowered her hand onto the rising bulge beneath his jeans. It began to throb as she massaged it with her palm.

Raymond was at his peak. Setting his hands free from underneath her skirt, he unzipped his pants, adjusted her panties, and entered her in one rushed motion. With an animalistic growl that vibrated from deep inside his throat, he grabbed her by the hips and thrust his manhood inside of her. Tammy lunged onto his lips, locking him in a kiss as he brought them both to climax simultaneously.

Out of breath, her heart beating fast, she remained still on his lap and rested her head on his shoulder, listening to his heavy breathing slowly subside to a normal pace.

After a moment of silence, Raymond shifted awkwardly in his seat beneath her. "Oh shit, Tammy, what did we just do?" There was a hint of remorse in his voice.

"Shhhh, it's okay. It can be our little secret," Tammy said as she pulled her skirt back down and tried to get back in her seat.

"Man, that was intense. I need a friggin' joint," Raymond confessed.

Tammy wrinkled her brow. "You need a what?"

"A joint...pot...marijuana? Don't tell me you've never heard of pot?" Raymond asked in disbelief while fumbling with his zipper.

"Nope, never. What is it?" she asked.

"Oh, Christ, you are so young and naive. I can't believe I'm telling you this. It's like a cigarette, but it makes you feel good and relaxed. It calms you. I don't know how else to describe it. But it's what I need right now."

Intrigued by what he'd just described, Tammy was anxious to try it. "That sounds great! I'd love to try some. Where is it? Let's smoke some now."

Amused by her innocence, Raymond chuckled. "I don't carry it on me, it's illegal. It's known as a drug and I only smoke it at home. It's not like cocaine or anything but it's still illegal."

Tammy was horrified. "It's a drug?" She had heard about drugs and how addictive they could be, but she'd never known anyone that used them.

"It's not as bad as it sounds. Let's go back to my place. I really do need one after what just happened. If you want to try it, that's up to you, but don't feel you have to," he told her as he straightened out his jeans and started up the car.

"Okay, we'll see," Tammy, replied with an innocent smile.

CHAPTER 13

ifteen minutes later, they were pulling into Raymond's long driveway, which was shaded by trees and bushes on either side. Tucked away from the street was his single-level duplex. Tammy was relieved to see he lived across town from her father's house and not close by.

During the drive, Raymond told her he was the property manager for the three duplexes in the building. In return, he got free rent. A young couple lived below him, and a single guy lived in the duplex behind him.

Once the truck was in park, Tammy picked her purse up from the floor, exited the car, and joined Raymond at the double glass doors where she found him fumbling with his keys. She chuckled at his nervousness and waited patiently while he struggled to open the door.

Once inside, she set her purse down on the long wooden table that separated the kitchen from the living room. Scattered across it were numerous coffee cups partially filled with stale coffee, a dirty ashtray, and a couple of empty soda cans. In the center was what Tammy assumed was Raymond's work area, consisting of building plans, a desk calculator, pens, and numerous business cards.

The off-white walls were in desperate need of a paint job, and the musty brown carpet with a few coffee stains had seen better days, too. Pictures of wildlife and outdoor scenes hung at random intervals on the walls. Both sides of the room had floor to ceiling windows, spanning the full length of the room. A faded beige couch sat in front of one window, while the other windows looked out onto a deck, with views across the main highway into Lones-ridge. The focal point of the room was a red brick fireplace. A television and an old comfy-looking chair with worn out tanned cushions were placed to its right.

Tammy quickly scanned the room before checking out the rest of the duplex while Raymond listened to his messages on the answering machine.

Walking through the main room and adjoining kitchen, she passed an office on the left and a bathroom on the right. At the end of the hallway was a dingy master bedroom. Chocolate-brown curtains were drawn closed, preventing natural sunlight from entering the dark space. She flicked the light switch on and saw it was a simple room with an unmade king-size bed against the back wall, which had oversized wooden tables on either side of it. A matching dresser and mirror sat across from the bed, disarrayed with loose change, odd socks, papers, and a variety of keys. The dirty laundry scattered on the floor amused her. Typical man, she thought.

When Tammy returned to the living room, she found Raymond sitting at the table talking business on the phone. She walked behind him, crossed her arms over his chest, and began nibbling on his ear. Unsuccessfully, he tried to brush her off while she quietly giggled behind him.

The odor of the cigarette smoldering in the ashtray next to him caught her attention. Now craving a cigarette herself, she released her hold on Raymond and grabbed his pack of Marlboro Reds sitting on the table, along with his yellow lighter. She left him to finish his work and made herself comfortable on the couch. Picking up the glass ashtray from the coffee table, she then lit the cigarette, inhaled deeply, and leaned back to savor the moment.

Raymond eventually ended his conversation and hung up the phone. Without saying a word, he disappeared into the kitchen and returned a few minutes later with a mason jar and a sheet of newspaper. He sat himself in the comfy chair, placed the newspaper on his knees, and twisted the lid off the jar.

"What's that?" Tammy asked, stubbing out her cigarette.

He smiled, held the jar up to the light and said, "This, my dear, is pot."

Intrigued, Tammy left the couch and knelt in front of him before leaning her arms on his knees to take a closer look. The jar was filled with light-green flakes of what looked like crumbled leaves. It reminded her of sage. She watched closely as he took a few pinches of the pot and placed it on the newspaper. From his top pocket, he took a pack of thin papers, pulled one out, and held it between his fingers.

"What are you doing?" Tammy asked.

"Making a joint."

With fascination, she continued to observe the process as he picked up pinches of the pot and sprinkled it evenly along the center of the paper. When he was finished, he moistened the edge with his lips, rolled it up like a cigarette and sealed it.

"Wow! That's cool. Can I try some?"

"Yeah, but not too much. Don't forget, I've got to take you home later." he said, smiling and pointing at her accusingly. "Let me show you how to smoke it. It's not like a cigarette. Watch me."

Tammy watched closely as he lit the end of the joint and inhaled deeply. "After you've taken a hit, hold your breath for a couple of seconds," Raymond instructed with a tight voice, indicating the smoke was still in his lungs. Then, he slowly exhaled while passing her the joint.

"Okay," she said, looking at the strange cigarette-like object between her fingers. She held it up to her nose and sniffed. "I love the way it smells," she said, wafting the scent into her nostrils like she'd just found a new favorite perfume. With a last curious glance at the joint, she slowly raised it to her lips, sucked a tentative drag, and inhaled deeply. Per Raymond's instructions, she held her breath.

Noticing the reddish tinge appearing on Tammy's puffed-out cheeks, Raymond said, laughing, "Okay, okay, you can let it out now! I only said a couple of seconds!"

After exhaling, she began to cough uncontrollably. "My god! That stuff is harsh," Tammy said, gasping for air.

"Don't worry. You'll get used to it," he said as she took another hit.

Tammy scowled at him in confusion. "I don't feel any different. What's supposed to happen?"

Raymond took the joint from her and finished it. "Give it a few minutes."

He was right. Shortly after, she began to feel the effects of the drug. Paranoia consumed her first. Feeling inexplicably fearful, she didn't like the sudden onset of insecure, unsettling emotions she was experiencing. Afraid to move or stand, she sat motionless on the floor, her knees up high under her chin, her legs locked in her arms.

She wanted to ask Raymond when would it end but was unable to speak, afraid her words would sound jumbled and not make any sense. Losing all her self-confidence and the ability to perform simple tasks, she yearned to feel normal again. *Why do people enjoy smoking this stuff when it makes you feel so awful?* Tammy decided she'd had enough. Feeling scared, she secretly made a promise to herself. *If I make it through this alive, I promise I will never smoke pot again.*

Next came the remorse and guilt. Knowing she was smoking an illegal drug, and therefore committing a crime, stunned her to the core. The notion that she may be caught and thrown in jail threw her head into a petrifying tailspin of horrific thoughts. Feeling ashamed, she wondered how she would ever face her father again. Still frozen by the drug, she kept reminding herself it would be over soon and everything would return to normal.

Slowly, after what seemed like an eternity, things were beginning to make more sense. Feeling more grounded thrilled her. She was able to move her arms and legs without fear and no longer felt threatened or scared. She felt like a warrior; triumph and victory had replaced her fears. She had preserved and beat the drug. She had won!

She turned her body to face Raymond and propped herself up on her knees. Feeling confident and strangely aroused, she leaned in and kissed him passionately on the lips. Then, it happened—triggered by the kiss—every nerve in her body exploded. She surrendered herself entirely to him. Her sexual energy and appetite was beyond anything she had ever experienced.

For a few moments, they caressed each other with force and hunger, but it wasn't enough. Within minutes, she lay naked on the floor, smothered by his sweat and scent, pinned by the weight of his body. "I want you," she whispered in his ear.

Hastily and with dynamic energy, Raymond thrust himself into her. Tammy released a loud, satisfying moan. Molded together as one, limbs intertwined, they quickly peaked and climaxed at the same time. But neither wanted it to end; they still had an appetite for more.

Tammy was now loving the drug and beginning to understand why people smoked it. She realized, now she'd worked her way through all the bullshit, that the resulting feeling was amazing. She didn't want it to end.

For the next couple of hours, they fondled, played, and explored every inch of each other's bodies. Tammy had lost count of the number of orgasms she'd had. She just knew she was feeling incredible. "Wow!" Tammy said breathlessly while lying naked in

Raymond's arms, trying to recuperate from yet another sensational climax. "That was amazing! Now I see why you like to smoke pot," she said, trying to contain a fit of giggles.

"It does have its advantages," Raymond chuckled. "God, Tammy. Your father can never find out about us. He would friggin' kill me," he added in a more serious tone.

"Does my dad know you smoke pot?"

"No, he doesn't. I guess there's a lot your father doesn't know about me."

"Well, Joanne seems to think you're a ladies' man. She told me you have a different woman every month. So, am I the flavor of the month?" Tammy teased.

"Oh, she does, does she? I didn't know she was paying that much attention to my love life. And no, silly, you're not the flavor of the month." Again, Raymond turned serious. "But we do have to be careful. We can't let anybody find out about us. Do you understand?"

Tammy sat up on her knees and faced him. "Don't worry, I won't tell anyone. I promise." She gave him a quick peck on his cheek and rose to her feet. "Now, come on. Let's get dressed so you can take me home."

CHAPTER 14

Over the next three months, Tammy and Raymond continued with their secret affair. Neither one dared to tell her father of their flourishing relationship, fearing his predictable, angered reaction would destroy all existing friendships.

Whenever Joanne didn't need Tammy's help, she would joyously skip the fifteen minutes across town to Raymond's place. He was always happy to see her. Never failing to greet her with a passionate embrace and a smile that warmed Tammy's heart. They cherished their secret afternoons together, never knowing when the next one would be.

Their meeting place was always at his home, never venturing out, afraid they may be seen by someone who knew her father. They made the most of their time together by drinking wine, smoking pot, and making love three or four times in an afternoon. They laughed and giggled like high school kids. For the first time since moving to the States, Tammy was finally having some fun.

But, a few days later, the fun came to a sudden halt. Tammy was facing a nightmare. "This can't be happening," Tammy cried out loud. She had bought three different brands and each one showed the same result. After lining them up on the bathroom counter, all of them revealed a pink "plus" sign. All three pluses jumped out at her from the thin plastic tubes—they may as well have been flashing neon signs—telling Tammy she was pregnant.

Feeling like she was going to faint, Tammy collapsed onto the seat of the toilet like a discarded rag doll. "Oh my god, how did this happen?" she whispered to herself. Of course, she knew how it happened, but she was on the pill and took one every morning. Then again, there was that one morning. It was about six weeks ago; Andrew fell, right before she was about to take it. She'd heard him scream from the living room and raced in to find he'd fallen into the coffee table. Joanne had got to him before she did.

The cut above his eye was deep so, fearing he may need stitches, they stopped whatever they were doing and rushed him to the hospital. In all the commotion, she'd forgotten to take her pill and didn't realize her error until the next morning when she saw she'd missed one. She took two that day to try and compensate, but it hadn't helped—obviously.

After having the three required stitches and returning from the hospital, Andrew slept most of the day, so Tammy had taken advantage and visited Raymond. She remembered they'd definitely had sex that afternoon, more than once. And now, here she was, eighteen and pregnant with his baby. She was too young to be having a child. She wasn't ready for this. She was just having some fun; it was never meant to be anything serious. What was she going to do? She had to tell him. How would he react to becoming a father?

She gasped out loud when she thought about her own father. Tammy knew she could never tell him, but how was she going to hide the pregnancy? The only person she could talk to was Raymond. She had no other friends. Feeling scared and completely alone, her mind raced a mile a minute with endless questions, to which she had no answers.

It'd been over six months since she arrived in the States. This was not how it was supposed to be. She came here on a mission to find Donna but was feeling deflated with nothing to go on and no new leads. Frustrations were at their peak. She had expected to have her independence, a car, a job, and a place to call her own by now. Tammy never imagined she would still be living with her father. But she didn't have a choice. She was still waiting for that damn green card. Without that, she couldn't work or drive. Now she found herself pregnant by her father's friend. Oh, what a mess her life had become.

Worried about her future, Tammy cradled her head in her arms and began to sob. Subconsciously, she rubbed her stomach, thinking of the tiny life growing inside of her. She had to think fast and decide what she was going to do. She needed to tell Raymond as soon as possible and ask his advice. They were in this together whether he liked it or not.

Tammy immediately knew an abortion was out of the question. The thought petrified her on so many levels. Adoption was not an option either. Never could she carry a child inside of her, feeling it grow and move, only to hand it over to complete strangers to raise as their own. No. Having this child was the only choice she had. Raymond would either support her or not. Tammy would just have to wait and see; either way, she was going to have this baby.

She realized, sadly, she could no longer live under her father's roof while pregnant with Raymond's child. She wasn't ready to tell him anything just yet, but when she did, the tension would become unbearable. Her only choice was to move in with Raymond.

Predicting her father's rage when the time came to tell him she was moving in with Raymond, Tammy decided to hide the pregnancy from him for a while; or at least until things had calmed down. Tammy could foresee her father feeling betrayed by Raymond, and probably her, too. She hated the thought of causing him pain. Over time, she hoped her father could forgive them and accept the child she was now carrying as his first and only grandchild. Suddenly, a loud knock at the door snapped her out of her thoughts.

"Hey, Tammy. Are you okay? You've been in there for a while. I need you to watch Andrew while I run to the store to get some milk," Joanne said from the other side of the door.

Startled by the intrusion, Tammy jumped up from the toilet seat in a panic and began scraping together all the pregnancy tests and packages that were spread across the counter. "Yes, I'm fine. I'll be out in a minute," she replied.

Tammy stared at the empty boxes, wondering where she could hide them. She had an idea. Bending down quickly, she opened the cupboard doors beneath the sink and grabbed the trash bag liner from the bin. She stuffed it with the rubbish she had accumulated and then tied the top into a knot. Placing the sealed bag on the counter momentarily, she checked herself in the mirror. Her eyes were reddish and she looked as white as a sheet, but all things considered, she didn't look too bad.

She splashed her face with cold water, applied some lipstick, and gave her hair a quick brush while trying to pull herself together. Satisfied with her appearance, she picked up the trash bag and slowly opened the door. Quietly, she peeked her head out and scanned the corridor left and right. Joanne was not in sight. Letting out a sigh of relief, she scurried to her room and stuffed the bag under her bed. She would deal with it later.

Feeling slightly more composed; she headed to the dining room, where she found Joanne sitting at the table bouncing Andrew on her knee. He was happily feasting on a cracker while spreading crumbs all over Joanne's lap.

Joanne stood up and handed Andrew over. "Thanks, Tammy. I won't be long," she said, brushing cracker flakes off her pants.

"No problem. I'll read him some books while you're gone."

As soon as Tammy heard the back door close, with Andrew still in her arms, she ran over to the kitchen window and looked out. From the window, she could see the garage clearly. The taillights came on and she heard the engine running. She watched and waited. A few minutes later, she saw Joanne back out of the garage and drive down the road into town.

Satisfied that the coast was clear, she quickly ran into her bedroom and gently placed Andrew on the bed while she knelt underneath and grabbed the trash bag. With her other hand, she scooped Andrew into her arm, resting him on her hip, and ran through the house to the back door.

She hurried down the steps to the metal trash cans lined up against the house. Removing the lid from the first one, she buried her bag of secrets among the others and replaced the lid. "Phew. That's done," she said, feeling relieved. She turned to her brother and held her finger up to her mouth, nuzzling his face with her nose as she whispered, "Shhh, it's our little secret. Okay?"

Andrew simply chuckled and smiled, apparently approving of the new game.

Feeling confident that the bag wouldn't be found, Tammy returned inside to read to Andrew.

CHAPTER 15

That night, unable to sleep, Tammy tossed and turned with endless thoughts about how her life had changed forever. Not only had she let herself down but also her father too. She dreaded seeing the dis- appointment on his face when she broke the news to him about her relationship with Raymond.

Ever since she was a child, his approval and praises have always been important to her. She yearned to see the pride in his eyes and smile. Like her father, Tammy had high hopes of going to college. The dream was now crushed due to her pregnancy. Disgusted with how her life was turning out and mortified that she was pregnant, she felt herself spiraling into a depressive state. She had no choice but to accept the new version of her life and the consequences it would bring regarding the relationship with her father.

With no sleep and her emotions in turmoil, Tammy was deter-mined to see Raymond early in the morning and break the news to him about the baby. His possible reaction feared her. She wasn't expecting him to be thrilled.

The next morning, Tammy dressed herself in jeans and a long-sleeved white cotton shirt, applied a little makeup, and brushed her hair. Not wanting to join Joanne for their usual morning cup of coffee and small talk, she needed to think of a reasonable excuse to leave early.

As predicted, Joanne was already sitting at the table reading the newspaper. She looked up when Tammy entered the room. "Hi, coffee is ready," she said with a smile.

Tammy stood nervously, fidgeting with her fingers. "Thanks, but I'm actually just on my way out."

"It's only nine o'clock," Joanne replied after glancing at her watch with a puzzled expression. "Where are you off to so early?"

Tammy thought quickly and blurted out the first thing that popped into her head. "I'm off to the library."

Annoyed with her lame excuse and anticipating the questions that would be likely to follow from Joanne—like why she needed to go to the library when they had so many books of their own— Tammy stalled. But, surprisingly, and thankfully, Joanne simply nodded and smiled.

She was tired of lying, especially to those close to her. The secret love affair she had with Raymond only existed because of her lies. It was the only way she could see him. At least if she moved in with Raymond, the lies would stop.

Relieved to be standing on the front porch with the door shut behind her, Tammy closed her eyes and took in a deep breath, feeling the cool, crisp air tingling her face. Bracing herself for the upcoming talk with Raymond, she found her confidence and began her walk.

Fifteen minutes later, she was knocking on his front door. With no answer, she tried the doorknob and found it unlocked, meaning he was home. Letting herself in, she heard the shower running from the bathroom. She peeked down the hallway and saw the bathroom door was slightly ajar. Clouds of steam from the shower hovered up high around the light. She chuckled while she listened to him bellowing the popular song *Yellow Submarine*. He sounded happy.

Tammy wondered if she was about to spoil his joyful mood. Or might she possibly enhance it? Remembering why she was there, a feeling of nausea crept over her, so she decided to wait for him outside on the deck to get some much-needed fresh air. A place where she could also contemplate how she was going to tell him the news of their child.

Sitting in the oversized wooden deck chair and smoking a cigarette, Tammy was lost in her thoughts. A tap at the window brought her back to reality. She turned to see Raymond looking out of the window, dressed in a blue bathrobe with a white towel draped around his neck. With a smile, he motioned for her to come inside.

Tammy forced herself to return the smile, stubbed out her cigarette, and left the deck to join him. Embracing her in his arms, Raymond gave her a light kiss on the cheek.

"What a pleasant surprise. Do you want some coffee?" he asked.

"Sure, that would be great. Thanks."

Raymond walked over to the kitchen and poured two cups of coffee while Tammy took a seat on the couch. Wondering how the hell she was going to tell him, she tried to make herself comfortable for the upcoming confession.

With two cups in one hand, Raymond took a seat next to Tammy and placed one of the mugs in front of her on the coffee table. "I thought I wasn't going to see you until tomorrow afternoon?" he asked before taking a sip of coffee.

Deciding not to beat around the bush and just tell him, Tammy ignored his question and dove right in. "Raymond, we have to talk."

Anticipating bad news and in fear of spilling his coffee, Raymond returned his mug to the table. "Okay, I'm listening. What's up?"

Before Tammy could reply, Raymond's body stiffened and his eyes opened wide with fear as he gasped. Thinking he had already guessed what she was about to tell him, Tammy nervously waited for his reaction. Sounding desperate, he grabbed her arm. "Don't tell me John knows about us. Please, don't tell me that!"

Tammy sighed; disappointed she'd still have to break the news.

"No, that's not it. But he's about to find out."

Raymond began to panic and tightened the grip on her arm.

"What do you mean? Who knows about us?"

"No one knows." Tammy took a long, deep breath to brace herself. "Raymond, there's no easy way to say this so I'm just going to come out and say it, okay? I'm pregnant." She sat in silence, watching every minute detail of his expression, waiting for him to say some- thing. Anything.

He pulled his hand away from her arm and let his body flop back against the couch. With a look of hopelessness, he simply stared straight ahead, stunned by the news. He said nothing.

After a few moments of silence, she nudged his knee with her hand.

"Raymond. Please say something."

Without reaching out to her or offering any kind of comfort, he finally spoke. "How did this happen? I thought you were on the pill."

"Well, yes, I am on the pill, but I missed one about six weeks ago. I tried to double up the next morning, but it obviously didn't help because...well, because I'm now pregnant."

"Can you get pregnant by missing one pill?" Raymond asked, looking puzzled.

"It sure looks like it, doesn't it?"

"Are you sure?"

"Yes, I'm sure. I brought three different tests and they all came up positive. What are we going to do?" Tammy asked, trying to hold back the tears. Seeking some kind of reassurance or support from the father of her unborn child, she reached for his hand. He simply brushed it away without saying another word.

Raymond stood and began pacing the room with both hands buried in his bathrobe pockets. "Let me think for a minute," he snapped, rubbing his forehead with the towel still draped around his neck. In an angered state, he began rummaging around and looking under papers on the dining room table, tossing them to the side by the handful.

"What are you looking for?" Tammy asked.

Raymond snapped again, "Where are my fucking cigarettes?"

"Here, have one of mine," Tammy quickly said, trying to calm him down. Reaching into her purse, craving a cigarette herself, she pulled out two and lit them both. She walked over to Raymond and handed him one. He took it from her with a hint of gratitude and sat at the table, pulling deeply on his smoke.

Tammy turned a chair to face him and slid into it with apprehension. Wanting to be closer to Raymond, she placed both her hands on his knees and leaned forward. "Before you do too much thinking, I should tell you that I've already decided I'm keeping the baby."

If he tried to hide his feelings of shock, it didn't work. Raymond's questions fired out in one long breath. "You are. But what about your dad? Do you honestly think he's going to accept a grandchild fathered by his friend who happens to be old enough to be his daughter's father? What do you think he's going to say about all this?" Raymond raised his voice a notch. "Come on, Tammy! There's no way! Admit it, we fucked up," he said, shaking his head in disbelief.

Tammy met his tone. "This isn't about my father anymore. This is about me, and the baby—*our* baby. I'm tired of trying to please him all the time. Of course he's not going to like the fact that I'm pregnant by you. It's not like I plan on telling him anytime soon. I'll be able to hide the pregnancy for a while. If you want nothing to do with me or the baby, that's fine, I understand." Tammy added a hint of sarcasm to her tone. "After all, you have a reputation in town to keep. I wouldn't want to embarrass you."

The fact that he was more concerned about her father's reaction angered her, but she still felt compelled to tell him her plan. "I've decided I'm going to have to move out of my father's house. There's no way I can stay there and have this child."

"And what do you plan on telling him?" Raymond asked.

"Well, I was hoping I could move in with you. In all honesty, I'm disappointed that you haven't asked me yet. I'm willing to tell my dad we're seeing each other and suffer the consequences. He'll probably be angry for a while, but give him some time and I'm sure he'll get over it. Living here with you, I'll be able to hide the pregnancy for a few months and give my dad some space to eventually accept us as a couple."

"You've given this some serious thought, haven't you?" Seeming calmer, he touched her for the first time since hearing the news. Leaning in toward her, he took her hands and held them tight under his chin before kissing her lightly on the forehead.

Tammy let out a huge sigh of relief. The kiss, no matter how small, meant so much to her at that moment. It told her he cared. "I really don't know what else to do. Do you have any ideas?" Tammy asked. Feeling she needed to remind him, she quickly added, "I won't have an abortion or give up the baby for adoption. I'll tell you that right now."

"I would never ask you to do that unless you wanted to. It seems your mind is made up. I guess I'm going to have to get use to the idea that I'm going to be a father. I've never imagined myself as one. Especially not now, at my age."

Raymond rested his arms on Tammy's shoulders and locked his hands behind her neck. Looking deep into her eyes, he unknowingly told her exactly what she had wanted, needed to hear. "Tammy, we're in this together. I'm on your side and I agree with you. Yes, I think it's a good idea that you come live here with me. But I must confess, it's going to be quite an adjustment for me. I've lived alone all my life. Your father, on the other hand, won't be okay with any of this. But, like you said, this is no longer about him. It's about us and the baby."

Listening to him speak, especially when he used the word *us*, brought tears to her eyes. As they trickled down her cheeks, Raymond softly wiped them away with his thumb. Tammy spoke, using a softer voice. "Thank you for being here with me...for me. It means a lot."

She wiped her moist cheeks with one of her hands and kissed Raymond softly on the lips. Caught up in the moment and stirred by the feeling of his tender lips on hers, she said, "I love you" for the very first time. Not sure if she truly meant those three little words, Tammy remained silent, anticipating Raymond's response.

He didn't acknowledge her confession. "It's okay," he said, wiping a loose strand of hair away from her eyes. "Have you thought about when you want to tell your father?"

Giving herself some more time to think about the answer, Tammy walked over to her purse and pulled out two more cigarettes before lighting them and returning to the table. She handed one to Raymond, which he gratefully accepted. "Joanne is a lot easier to talk to than my dad. Maybe I should talk to her first. Honestly, my dad scares me. She'll probably give me some good advice on how to approach him. What do you think?"

Raymond didn't know what to say. The only thing he could do was to agree with her. "Sounds like a good idea to me."

Tammy continued with her plan. "I think it's best I do this on my own. No offense, but I'm sure they won't want to see you for a while."

Relieved at knowing he wouldn't have to face John, Raymond agreed without so much as a second thought, just in case she changed her mind. "I'm the last person your father will want to see. Once you tell him, our friendship will be destroyed forever."

"I know. I'm sorry. Collateral damage, I guess." Not wanting to dwell on that particular subject, Tammy added to her plans. "So, I'm going to talk to Joanne as soon as I get home. Hopefully, my dad will still be at the office. I want to get this over with as soon as possible and get out of there. I know, once I tell them, I'll have to leave right away. It'll just be too unbearable to stay any longer." She took his hand and squeezed it hard. "I know we can make this work, Raymond. I know I can't get a job right now, but I can help you manage the duplexes here and—"

Raymond raised his arm, interrupting her. "Whoa, slow down, girl, one step at a time. Let's get through the hardest part first, which is telling your dad and moving you in here, before we start making any more plans. Okay?"

"Yes, okay. You're right. You're right. I'm getting ahead of myself. Sorry." She feigned a slap across her wrist and laughed nervously. "Oh no! I just had a thought."

"What?" he asked, suddenly looking worried.

"How am I going to get my things over here? My dad sure as hell won't help me and I can't ask Joanne." She paused, letting the realization sink in. "Oh jeez, you're going to have to come get me."

"Me!"

"Yes, you. I don't know anyone else." Seeing the look of horror on his face, Tammy tried to reassure him. "You won't have to come in the house. You can just wait in the truck."

Raymond became panicked again. "Oh, Jesus Christ! This is getting harder by the minute." In a flustered state, he stood and began pacing the room. He stopped in mid-stride and turned and faced Tammy. "You're just going to have to leave when John isn't home. If he knew I was waiting outside, he'd come out and probably kill me!" He walked back to the table, stubbed out his cigarette and immediately lit another one from a pack he found among the piles on the table.

"Good idea! I'm going to have to call you when it's time for you to come pick me up. God, I'm dreading this. I can't wait till I'm here with you and all this is behind us."

Seeking comfort, Tammy left her chair and walked over to Raymond. He welcomed her into his arms and held her tight. Fearing what lay ahead, neither of them wanted to let go. With eyes closed, they stood in silence, holding each other for some time until Tammy forced herself to back away, knowing she had to leave and face the music.

"I'd better go," she said as she began searching for her purse, which she found by the couch and slung it over her shoulder. "Oh! I've just remembered I need to stop at the library."

"The library? You're thinking about reading books at a time like this? Can't it wait until you've moved out?"

"No, it's not that," Tammy laughed. "I'm covering up another lie. It's a long story, and I need to get going. Listen, I'll call you later and tell you how it went, okay?" She paused. "Wish me luck."

At the door, Raymond held her in his arms once more and kissed her gently on the lips. He couldn't help but think about the volcano that was about to erupt as he watched her walk down the driveway. Before long, she'd be on her way to his soon-to-be-loathed-by dear friends, John and Joanne. No longer will he be welcomed in their home. News of his relationship with his daughter would soon spread throughout the town. Fearing the locals' reaction, he knew without a doubt that his relationship with Tammy was going to cost him many more friendships.

His life was about to change forever. He was going to be a father, but not by choice. He only agreed to Tammy moving in with him because it was the right thing to do. In his entire life, he had never lived with a woman. The idea of sharing his world and his private space didn't appeal to him in the slightest. Joanne was right. He was a player. Having a serious relationship—or worse, marriage—scared the hell out of him.

Wondering what he had gotten himself into, he didn't know if he could do it. Raymond questioned why she declined the option to have an abortion. It certainly would have prevented this whole mess. Feeling trapped and pushed into a corner against his will, he couldn't help but feel this was the biggest fuck-up of his life.

Tammy turned and waved one last time as she disappeared from the end of the driveway into the street. He unconsciously waved back, forced a smile, and returned inside to wait for her call.

CHAPTER 16

*I*n no hurry to return home, Tammy spent the afternoon wandering aimlessly around the town, mainly contemplating how she was going to break the news to Joanne. She shuddered at the thought of her likely reaction. After procrastinating for a few hours, she finally found the courage to head home. Once on the front porch, she took a deep breath to calm her rattled nerves before opening the door.

Inside, she found Joanne sitting at the dining room table reading a book.

"Hi, Joanne," Tammy said softly, not wanting to startle her.

Removing her glasses, Joanne looked up. "Hi, hon, how was the library?"

"Oh, I didn't go in the end. Is Andrew taking a nap?"

"Yes, I just put him down." Sensing something was wrong, Joanne looked closer at Tammy. "Are you okay? You look upset."

Tammy joined her at the table. Sitting across from her she realized Joanne knew her too well to try and cover up any more secrets and lies, Tammy knew it was time to tell the truth. "Is Dad home?" she asked, wanting to make sure they were alone before she went any further.

"No, he'll be in his office all day. He has a deadline to meet." Joanne was visibly worried. "What's going on, Tammy?"

Thankful that her father wasn't home, she took the plunge. "Joanne, I have to tell you something." She paused, trying to choose her words carefully. "Well, Dad too, but I want to tell you first. Dad scares me." She chuckled, trying to add a little humor to their otherwise awkward conversation.

Joanne laid down her book, giving Tammy her full attention. "Okay, what's up?"

Trembling to her core with nerves, Tammy extended her arms out on the table and clenched her fists. With a forlorn look, she began her speech for the second time. "There is no easy way to say this, so I'm just going to come out and say it."

"Okay," Joanne said, sounding both concerned and suspicious.

Tammy took another deep breath. "I've been seeing Raymond," she blurted. There, she'd said it. It was now out in the open. Letting out a huge sigh of relief, Tammy felt her body being drained of the all-consuming secret she'd been keeping for months.

They sat in silence while Tammy anxiously waited for any reaction from Joanne. Surprisingly, Joanne didn't flinch a muscle. When she spoke, her tone was flat, measured, and her voice was calm. "Seeing him in what way? Are you friends? Are you dating? Have you had sex with him?"

Tammy hesitated. "I've been seeing him since he took me to the Gold Rush town. And yes, we've had sex." Each time she released another secret, her shoulders felt a little lighter as the weight of the burden continued to drain away.

Joanne remained calm. "I see. Although, I must admit, I've had my suspicions."

"You have?" Since when?" Tammy felt heat rising over her cheeks.

"Since your first outing together. When you came home, you seemed...different. Your mannerism was different, your..." Pausing mid-sentence, she changed her tone, raising it a notch. "Okay, I'll be blunt. You looked like a woman that just had sex."

Shocked by Joanne's raw honesty, Tammy was unable to find any words. She listened to Joanne explain her reasoning.

"I could read triumph and satisfaction all over you. And you walked around with a stupid smirk on your face, acting silly and much happier than usual. In fact, there have been many times you've come home acting that way."

Tammy knew part of her silliness was due to smoking pot. But she'd be happy to keep carrying the weight of that particular secret.

She still had more to tell Joanne. "I'm sorry for lying to you, but I've been afraid to tell you and Dad...especially Dad. The reason I'm telling you now is because I want to move in with Raymond."

Up until now, Joanne had managed to stay calm through Tammy's confessions. It hadn't been easy, but she could feel herself slowly losing control. She had to talk some sense into the girl. "Oh my, Tammy, I wasn't expecting to hear that. Have you talked to Raymond about this?"

"Yes, and you probably figured out some time ago that I wasn't at the library today. I was with him, discussing how I was going to tell you guys."

"I don't understand. Why the rush to move in with him? Do you love him?"

Tammy didn't answer and instead looked down at the table.

"Well, you can't love him if you have to think about it." With a short intake of breath, she suddenly sat bolt upright in her chair. She stiffened her lip and used a sharper tone. "Wait, Tammy. Are you pregnant?"

"Absolutely not!" she said, raising her voice slightly to add drama to her reply. So much for letting go of all the secrets and lies, she thought.

Joanne relaxed back in her chair as her anxieties dropped a few levels. "Well, that's a relief. I can't imagine what this is going to do to your father. He'll probably never want to speak to Raymond again. What was he thinking? He's old enough to be your father, for Christ's sake," she said, shaking her head in disbelief.

"It wasn't entirely his fault, please don't blame him," she begged, squirming slightly in her seat. "We never planned for any of this to happen. It just did. He feels terrible, and he's already quite certain Dad will never speak to him again, but we can't pretend nothing happened."

Joanne was still confused. "Well, why the rush to move in with him? Why upset your father?"

Tammy had to think quickly, her answer needed to sound convincing. "To be honest, I'm tired of sneaking around and lying to you both. To come out and tell you wasn't easy for me, but it needed to be done. And, now that you know, it's going to be too uncomfortable for me to carry on living here. I wouldn't be able to mention his name or talk about him. Besides, I need my independence back. It's been hard living with parents again." Unable to hold back the tears anymore, Tammy's body began to tremble as the sadness she was feeling poured out of her. "We never meant to hurt you or Dad, but we think it would be best if I moved in with him."

Joanne felt her pain and at least showed some sympathy by retrieving a box of tissues from the bookshelf and placing them in front of Tammy. Crying uncontrollably, Tammy pulled out a tissue and hid her face in shame. Knowing she had disappointed the two most important people in her life brought her to a crumbling state. After dabbing her eyes, Tammy spoke, her voice weak. "Thank you. I'm so sorry. I don't know how I'm going to tell Dad. You're much easier to talk to, and look at me, I'm already a wreck."

Seeing the poor girl so distraught, Joanne felt the need to console her. Reaching out, she gave her shoulder a tender squeeze.

"Don't you worry about your father for now, okay? But, I must be honest with you, I think you're making a huge mistake."

Tammy sniffed and looked up. "You do?"

"Yes, I do. You're so young. You've just turned eighteen. You have your whole life ahead of you. You've been in this country for less than a year and you want to be with some guy who is twice your age and move in with him for all the wrong reasons. When you decide you want to share your life with someone, it's because you love them, and want to be with them. You haven't even said you love him. Neither I, nor your father can tell you what to do. I just hope you realize how foolish you're being." Joanne knew her words were harsh, but it was her last attempt to talk some sense into her.

Refusing to make eye contact, Tammy held her head low; listening closely to every word Joanne was saying and knowing they were true.

Joanne's tone became softer. "You know, your father may not show it, but he thinks the world of you and your sisters. He feels guilty for being away so much when you were younger. He has always wanted the best for all of you. He's haunted by Donna's disappearance and blames himself entirely."

"Why does he blame himself?" Tammy asked, finally looking at Joanne.

Joanne leaned forward. "Think about it. If he had never brought Donna to the States, she wouldn't have run away."

Tammy never realized how much her father was hurting. He was not one to express his emotions, but strangely enough, it appeared he had shared some of his feelings with Joanne. Tammy knew she would be adding to his pain by moving in with not just a guy, but a man he had trusted. A man he thought was his friend but was now dating his youngest daughter. Tammy couldn't suppress the guilt descending on her conscience. She couldn't deny her fear of possibly becoming estranged from her father. But what choice did she have? She was pregnant with Raymond's child.

Joanne interrupted Tammy's internal dialogue. "And I hate to tell you this, but your dad will probably blame himself for this too."

"Why would you say that?" Tammy asked, confused by her remark.

"Because he brought you here, just like Donna, and he introduced you to Raymond."

"I'm sorry, I just don't know what else to do. I want to keep seeing Raymond, but I can't if I continue to live here. It's not Dad's fault and I don't want him to think it is."

"I know, sweetheart, and if this is what you really want then, well, we can't stop you." Joanne reached out and gently squeezed her arm. "Leave it to me. I'll talk to your father."

"You will?" Tammy questioned, surprised by her gesture.

"Yes, I will. But, honestly, I don't think you should be here when I do."

"You don't? Why not?"

"Because I don't want your dad to say something to you that he may regret. I'm not sure how he's going to react to all this. Why don't you go back to Raymond's tonight? You can call me in the morning after your dad has left for the office. I think that will be best."

"Joanne, I hate to leave this all up to you. I've made such a mess of everything." Unable to control another wave of tears, Tammy reached for a dry tissue from the box.

Caving into Tammy's distraught manner, Joanne left her seat to console her. Tammy stood, reaching out with her arms to welcome her caring hug.

"Shhh, it's okay, everything will be okay," Joanne said, stroking Tammy's freshly mangled hair.

Rising from her tears, Tammy shook her head to compose herself. "Thanks for everything. I love you," she told Joanne.

"I love you too. Now, Andrew will be waking up soon. Why don't you go pack a bag and head over to Raymond's? I'll speak to you in the morning."

Without hesitation, fearing her father may soon return, Tammy hastily grabbed a few things from her room, said goodbye, and left.

CHAPTER 17

On the other side of the closed door, Tammy's emotions peaked. Thinking of the terrible possibilities that lay ahead and slowly becoming hysterical, she sprinted through town, oblivious to the innocent members of public she mowed down along the way. Thankfully, her tears shielded her from the startled looks of disgust on the faces of those in her path.

She arrived at Raymond's in just eight minutes, exhausted and out of breath. Relieved to find the door unlocked, Tammy rushed inside.

"Raymond! Raymond! Are you here?" she yelled, kicking the door closed with her foot and throwing her bags on the dining room table.

Alarmed and scared, Raymond came rushing down the hallway. Meeting him halfway, Tammy raced into his arms. "Oh, Raymond, I've made such a bloody mess of things."

Raymond tried to console her as she continued to cry heavily on his shoulder. "Hey now, calm down. Tell me what happened," he said in a soothing voice.

Letting her tears subside, Tammy wiped her reddened eyes on

her sleeve, pulled herself together, and began telling Raymond about her conversation with Joanne.

"It was horrible and I feel bloody awful about everything. Joanne offered to tell my dad. I couldn't say no," Tammy confessed. "She also thought it would be best if I stayed here for the night. I hope that's okay?"

"Of course it's okay. You don't have to ask me. Do you want a beer?" Raymond asked, craving one himself.

"I shouldn't really, because of the baby, but it will help calm my nerves," she replied.

Taking a seat on the couch, Tammy leaned back and closed her eyes. After grabbing two beers from the kitchen, Raymond placed them on the coffee table and joined her. He stared at her with pity. She looked lost and withdrawn. Wrapping his arm around her shoulder, he was glad to see Tammy welcomed the hug and leaned into his body, resting her head on his chest.

Embraced together in silence, they consoled each other while trying to process the current events unfolding in their lives. Both unsure of their futures and questioning their now fragile relationship with Tammy's father, they were feeling ashamed and embarrassed. Tammy fearing she may lose her father and Raymond wondering how he could ever face John again. His once great friendship was now dissolved because of his stupid, selfish actions. He knew John would never be able to forgive him. Neither Tammy nor Raymond chose to share their private concerns with each other. Instead, they remained somber and quiet until it was time to go to bed.

After a restless night of worry, Tammy woke early the next morning. Being careful not to wake Raymond, she tiptoed across the bedroom and wrapped herself in his bathrobe before going to make coffee. She was thinking, by now, Joanne had probably told her dad everything. So many questions ran through Tammy's mind. How did he take it? Should she call him? Will he call her?

Tired of the miserable rut she was in, Tammy forced herself to take a shower and then dressed herself in jeans and a blue tank top. Feely mildly better, she focused on calling Joanne after Raymond had left. She was anxious to hear how her father had reacted, although she feared the worst.

Soon, Raymond was up and talking business on the phone in his office. Tammy kept herself busy by cleaning the kitchen. A half- hour later, he came out of the office and grabbed his jacket from the back of one of the chairs. "I have to go do an estimate. I'll be back in a couple of hours," he told her as he headed toward the front door.

"That's fine. I'll probably still be here when you get back," she replied, ushering him out.

Mid-stride, Raymond turned and gave her a quick peck on the cheek. Tammy returned the gesture and watched him scurry to his truck.

Within minutes of him leaving, Tammy raced to the office, sat at the desk, and dialed her father's house number, praying it wouldn't be him that answered. Holding her breath, she listened to the phone ring a few times and then, to her relief, she heard Joanne's voice. "Hello."

Tammy relaxed and exhaled. "Hi, Joanne, it's Tammy."

"Hi, hon," Joanne said softly.

Not wanting to deal with small talk, Tammy cut to the chase. "Did you talk to Dad?" she asked, anxiously gripping the phone with both hands.

Joanne's voice was flat, telling her what she had feared. "Yes, I did speak to him. I'm not going to lie to you, your father's upset. And, like I suspected, he blames Raymond far more than you. He thinks you're young and naive, but that doesn't mean to say he's not upset with you as well. I won't repeat what he called Raymond —it'll only upset you—but I must say, in all the years I've been with your father, I've never heard him use such language before."

Tammy began to fret. If her father had such hatred based only on the relationship, how was she ever going to tell him about the baby? "What should I do?" Tammy asked. "Should I come over there or should I call him on the phone?"

Joanne sighed. "Well, your father doesn't want to see you right now."

"What?"

"He needs to calm down and accept this in his own time. It may take him a while and, if I were you, I wouldn't rush him. Let him call you when he's ready."

Tammy couldn't believe her father didn't want to see her. "Does he hate me?"

"No, he doesn't hate you. You're his daughter. He's just upset right now. He'll come around eventually. Just give him some time."

Tammy was astonished. She didn't realize how much this was going to hurt her father. Their relationship had always been good and they'd never experienced any conflicts, up until now. Lost in her thoughts, Tammy's head buzzed with questions and fears. Mainly, she feared her father would never forgive her.

"Tammy, are you still there?"

"Yeah, I'm still here," Tammy replied in a solemn voice.

"What shall I do about your things? Your father won't be home until tonight, so you can come by and get them any time before then." Joanne's voice became stern. "But I must ask, out of respect for your dad, that Raymond does not come in the house."

"I understand." Tammy had another thought. "Should I call before coming over?"

"Yes, I think it would be best." There was silence. "Tammy, are you okay?"

Tammy held back her tears. "No, I'm not okay. I didn't mean to hurt you or Dad, and I'm truly sorry. Will you tell him that and tell him I love him? I need to go. I'll call you later."

"Okay. You take care of yourself. We love you, too," Joanne told her, knowing she needed to hear it.

After Tammy hung up the phone, she leaned over the desk and buried her tearstained face in her folded arms.

Later that afternoon, when Raymond returned, they spoke about her conversation with Joanne. For Raymond, it was now real —John had ended their friendship. But he hadn't expected him to take such actions with his daughter. He agreed with Joanne that Tammy just needed to give her father some time.

After Raymond had been updated, Tammy called Joanne to let her know they were on their way to pick up her things. Joanne reminded her again that she must collect her belongings on her own.

Leaving Raymond in the truck, Tammy approached the front door of her father's house. Strangely, it no longer felt like home. Wondering if she should knock, Tammy paused for a moment. Deciding against it, she slowly turned the doorknob and let herself in. Feeling awkward and alienated, Tammy wanted this to be over with as soon as possible. She spotted Joanne, her back toward her, watering plants at the dining room window. "Hi, Joanne."

Joanne turned, placing the green watering can on the table and crossed the room to meet her. "Hi, sweetie, you okay?" Joanne asked while giving her a hug.

Tammy lied. "Yeah, I'm fine."

Reaching behind the kitchen door, Joanne handed Tammy some canvas bags. "Here, you can use these to put your things in."

"Thanks," Tammy said softly before heading to what was now her old room. Thankful she didn't have much to pack, Tammy crammed her belongings in two bags with speed and returned to the dining room with a bag in each hand.

Approaching the table, where Joanne was reading a book to Andrew in her lap, Tammy placed the bags at her feet. "I'm all done. Can I ask you something?"

Joanne removed her glasses. "Sure. What is it?"

Even though Tammy was apprehensive, she had to ask. "I know Dad doesn't want to see me right now, and I respect that, but would it be possible to come visit you and Andrew when he's not home?"

Joanne gave her a smile. "I don't see why not. Why don't you call me in a few days after things have settled down and we'll see what we can arrange. Okay?"

With Andrew still in her lap, Joanne remained seated. Tammy leaned over and gave her a hug. "Thanks, I will." Crouching down lower, she squeezed her brother's cheek. "Bye, little guy. I'll see you soon," she promised.

Joanne took her hand. "You take care of yourself and remember we both love you. Your father just needs some time to adjust."

Shaken, Tammy could only manage a nod. She retrieved her bags and left out the front door, closing it quickly behind her to prevent Joanne from seeing her shiny, wet eyes.

Once in the truck, her tears fell endlessly. Not knowing what to do, Raymond reached over and held her tight. Tammy cried hard, releasing the pain, the regrets of her actions, and the unknowns of her future. When she had no more tears to shed, she released herself from Raymond's arms, leaned back in her seat and stared out of the window, mellowing deep in her own thoughts. If she had stayed in England, none of this would have happened. She wouldn't be pregnant and she would still have a relationship with her father. Filled with guilt and remorse, Tammy wondered if coming to the States was a mistake.

CHAPTER 18

*L*iving with Raymond was not how Tammy had imagined. She'd rarely seen him in the six weeks since she'd moved in. Within days, he had thrown himself into his work, leaving at the crack of dawn and not returning until after dark. It almost felt like he was purposely avoiding her. Rarely did they speak. With no affection or lovemaking between them, the relationship had turned dry and they both knew they were only together because of the baby.

Realizing Joanne had been right, Tammy knew she was with Raymond for all the wrong reasons. She'd let panic and fear guide her and had made the wrong decisions as a result. With the benefit of hindsight, Tammy now realized telling Raymond she loved him was a mistake—fueled only by emotions and impulse—when what they had really shared was nothing more than pure lust. Sneaking around, lying, and the thrill of doing the forbidden, along with the risk of getting caught, had added danger and excitement to their newly founded affair. They smoked a lot of pot, laughed a lot, and had a lot of sex. In the early days, they had enjoyed the peril that came with the relationship.

Tammy had not spoken to her father in over six weeks. Each time the phone rang, her heart skipped a beat in the hopes that it was him. But it never was. She missed him being in her life. She missed being his daughter.

Guessing she was ten or twelve weeks pregnant, Tammy had growing concerns that she hadn't yet seen a doctor for confirmation or the well-being of the baby. Still trying to protect his image, Raymond had insisted they see a doctor in one of the larger towns, south of Lonesridge. The nearest one was about an hour away. With the promise that he would take her soon, Tammy avoided asking him again.

Raymond showed little interest in the baby. He never expressed any sense of joy or excitement, and rarely did he ask how she and the baby were doing. In her heart, Tammy knew it was over. But she was stuck; she had nowhere else to go. She was just buying time until she could figure out what to do next.

After moping around one morning, still dressed in her blue bathrobe and slippers, Tammy decided she was going to make her day constructive. Letting out a groan, she pulled herself up from the couch. With her body feeling suddenly heavy, her legs weak and numb, she used the arm of the couch to stabilize herself before heading to the bathroom to take a shower.

Overcome with dizziness, she rested at the kitchen counter. A sharp, cramping pain in her abdomen caused Tammy to hold her stomach while straining to make it the rest of the way.

She slowly lowered her body into a sitting position on the closed toilet seat. Assuming the pain was part of the pregnancy, Tammy rested her head on her knees, hoping it would ease the pain. "It'll soon pass," she told herself. But it didn't. She began to panic. Something wasn't right. Beads of sweat formed on her brow. Her sweaty palms itched. In need of a towel, she slowly stood up. That's when she saw the blood on the seat of the toilet. Horrified, she looked down at her body and saw the large patch of soiled blood on her nightgown. Trickles of red liquid ran down the insides of her legs and spotted the floor around her feet.

"Oh my god! I'm losing the baby!" Tammy cried.

Overcome with fear and exhaustion from the emotions ripping through her body, Tammy fell to her knees and wept. She wished she weren't alone. Over her tears, she heard the phone ring from the office. Was it Raymond? Knowing she wouldn't be able to make it before the answering machine came on, Tammy managed to calm herself down and subside her breathing so she could focus on listening instead.

After four rings, the machine clicked on and asked the caller to leave a message.

Tammy held her breath. Will they leave a message?

She heard a cough and then... "Hi, Tammy, it's your dad." He spoke in a cold, stiff voice, expressing no emotion.

"Daddy! Oh my god, it's my dad!" Tammy screamed, knowing he couldn't hear her because she couldn't get to the phone. She strained her ears to listen to the rest of his message.

"Your papers came in from immigration and you have an interview with them in two weeks in San Francisco. Because I'm your sponsor, I'll need to accompany you. Joanne has all the details regarding the date and time, so I'd appreciate it if you would give her a call. Goodbye."

The answer machine sounded a final beep, followed by silence.

Hearing that her father hadn't asked how she was and said he wanted her to call Joanne and not him, made Tammy realize he was still angry. If it weren't for the immigration issue, he would never have called.

With increasing pains and nausea, Tammy managed to crawl to the toilet and raise the lid. Still on her knees, she held her gut while she retched violently into the bowl. With great effort and through her agony, Tammy found the strength to run a hot bath. She crawled into the tub to soak her exhausted and bloodied body, hoping to ease the excruciating pain. Being engulfed in the soothing warm water brought a sense of calmness and slowly washed away her aches and pains until she drifted off to sleep.

Having lost all sense of time, the chilled water woke her with a start. Shivering but now with less pain, Tammy stepped out of the bathtub, being careful to avoid the bloody towels strewn across the floor. Her trembling legs still felt weak beneath her as she wrapped herself in a clean towel and slowly made her way to the darkened bedroom to lie down.

CHAPTER 19

*R*eturning home at dusk, Raymond questioned why the house was in complete darkness. He flicked on the light by the front door and threw his keys on the dining room table, surveying the apparently empty duplex. "Tammy, are you home?"

Greeted by silence, Raymond didn't know what to think. Where could she be? She has nowhere else to go. Concerned, he headed to check the bathroom and bedroom. He turned on the light in the darkened bathroom and gasped when he saw the bloody towels scattered in disarray across the floor. Fear and anxiety swept through him. "Tammy!" he yelled. There was no answer. "Tammy!" Still, no answer. Fearing the worst, he stepped away from the bathroom, took a deep breath, and prepared himself for something bad as he made his way toward the bedroom.

Like the rest of the house, the room was dark. He fumbled for the light switch, found it and turned it on, instantly relieved to see Tammy's outline curled under the covers. Not wanting to startle her, Raymond tiptoed across the room, crouched down beside her, and gently shook her shoulder. "Tammy, it's me, Raymond," he whispered. She didn't move. "Tammy," he said, louder this time. "Tammy, wake up! Are you okay?"

Tammy began to stir from her deep sleep. Opening her eyes slowly, she felt the warmth of Raymond's breath on her cheek.

"Are you okay?" Raymond asked again as he brushed the mop of damp hair from her face.

Grabbing his hand, Tammy buried her face in his palm. "No. Raymond, I lost the baby." That was all she managed to say before bursting into tears.

Raymond was alarmed by her news. "My god! What...how... are you okay?" he stammered in confusion as he lay down next to her. He cradled her in his arms, holding her tenderly while she pressed her face against his chest and wept uncontrollably.

It took Tammy a few minutes to compose herself before she was able to talk.

Raymond pulled himself up to a sitting position while still holding her. "Do you need to go see a doctor?" he asked.

Tammy shook her head. "No, I'm okay. It was early in the pregnancy. I should be fine. I managed to take a hot bath and sleep most of the day." Shedding more tears, Tammy gripped Raymond's arm and squeezed it tight. "Oh, Raymond, it was awful. I felt so scared. There was nothing I could do. I feel terrible. It's all my fault. The baby didn't feel wanted. I showed it no love and that's why it left me."

"Hey now, don't be so hard on yourself. It wasn't your fault at all. Unfortunately, these things happen," he said, trying to reassure her. "Hey, do you want a cup of tea?"

The thought comforted Tammy. "Sure, that sounds good. Thanks."

Before leaving, he helped her up to a sitting position and puffed up the pillows behind her back and neck. "There. How's that?" he asked. "Want to watch some TV?" He grabbed the remote from the dresser as he walked by and aimed it at the television. "It will help take your mind off all this crap," he said. Once the TV came on, he tossed the remote to Tammy. "Watch whatever you want. I'll back in a few minutes."

As promised, Raymond returned a few minutes later with a hot cup of tea and placed it on the bedside table. Tammy smiled and leaned over to retrieve the mug, feeling the warmth as she cradled it in her hands. After taking a sip, she closed her eyes and lay back, letting the calming tea soothe her. Mother was right, Tammy thought to herself; she always used to say, "Never underestimate the power of a cup of tea."

Raymond joined Tammy on the bed and cradled her in his arms again. Both lost in their own thoughts and saddened by the events of the day, they lay together in silence. In addition to the guilt that was consuming her, Tammy was feeling a huge void. One she knew could never be filled.

Keeping his thoughts to himself—mainly because he was too ashamed to admit them—he was feeling a sense of relief that Tammy had lost the baby. He'd never imagined himself as a father or family man.

Tammy interrupted his shameful thoughts, speaking in a soft whisper. "My dad called today."

Alarmed, Raymond sat up to face her. "He did? What did he say?"

"I didn't speak to him. I was in the bathroom and couldn't get to the phone in time, but I heard him over the answering machine."

Raymond was getting impatient. "And?"

"He only called to let me know I have an interview with immigration in two weeks and that he must go with me. He wants me to call Joanne and make arrangements with her." Tammy raised her voice, slightly. "Not *him* I might add. He specifically said Joanne. He doesn't care about me. If it wasn't for the interview, he would never have called."

"Well that's good news, isn't it? You've been waiting a long time for an interview." Raymond paused. "At least you won't have to tell him about the baby."

Infuriated by his remark, Tammy raised her voice. "God, Raymond, you are so fucking insensitive! Is that all you care about? Your reputation with my dad? Don't you get it? He hates you. You fucked his youngest daughter! It doesn't matter that I don't have to tell him about the baby. It still won't change the fact that he ended his friendship with you, and trust me, he will *never* forgive you."

Tammy threw the empty cup hard on the floor next to the bed and heard it shatter. She flung the blankets away from her body, pulled herself up, and slid off the bed in a string of deliberately dramatic movements. Placing her hands on her hips, she glared at Raymond. "Are you not the least bit upset that we lost the baby? Or are you relieved, Raymond? Tell me the truth," she snarled at him.

Startled by her sudden anger and with chilling thoughts of what might happen if he told her the truth, he quickly uttered, "I was getting used to the idea of being a father. Yes, granted, I wasn't overjoyed when you first told me. I was in shock. You have to admit, neither one of us planned or remotely thought this would ever happen." He sat nervously on the edge of the bed, anxiously waiting for her next outburst.

Not knowing whether to believe him or not and still consumed with anger, she stormed over to the closet, grabbed her bathrobe from the door, wrapped it around herself, and jerked the belt into a tight knot. "I'm going out on the deck. I need some fresh air." Without looking back, she stormed out of the bedroom and slammed the door behind her.

Feeling a slight breeze from the evening skies, Tammy sat quietly on the wooden chair as she tried to calm down. Leaves ruffled above her head in the surrounding trees and in the distance, she heard the occasional car drive by on the highway. Thinking about how much she had fucked everything up and how fucked up her entire life was in general; she felt her mood transitioning into a depressive state. Not knowing what to do next, Tammy stared aimlessly at the full moon above her.

The squeaking sound of the screen door behind her interrupted her thoughts. Glancing over her shoulder, she saw Raymond precariously holding two glasses of red wine.

"Hey, thought you might like a glass of wine," he said. "It might make you feel better."

Having finally calmed down after her explosive exit, Tammy appreciated his caring gesture and gladly took a glass. "Thank you," she said in a much friendlier tone.

Taking baby steps, not quite sure of her mood, Raymond eased himself slowly into the deck chair beside her and took a sip of his drink before placing his hand gently on her knee. "I'm sorry if I upset you," he said. "I didn't mean to, and yes, you're right about your father. He'll never forgive me. I'm trying to wrap my head around it. We've been friends for so long."

Taking his hand in hers, Tammy gave it a slight squeeze, followed by a tender kiss, knowing he was trying his best to comfort her.

"I'm sorry too," she said. "I was feeling alone and scared. I was angry because you weren't here when I was losing the baby." Not wanting to start another argument, Tammy quickly added. "But it's not your fault. How were you to know?" Tammy paused, thinking carefully about her next words. "And, to be completely honest, I don't know what's going to happen between us now. We both know the only reason I moved in with you is because of the baby. I wouldn't be here if I hadn't got pregnant. Now that I'm not, where does that leave us?"

Raymond stood up and squeezed her hand, followed by a tug, gesturing her to follow him. "Let's not get into that now. You need your rest," he said with a kind smile. "Why don't you crawl back into bed, watch a movie, and I'll bring you some nice warm chicken soup, okay?"

Knowing he was right, Tammy wasn't going to argue. She

gladly took his advice and followed him to the bedroom, carrying the glass of wine in her free hand. Noticing Raymond had cleaned up the shattered cup from the floor, she set her glass next to his on the end table and waited for him to rearrange her pillows before crawling back into bed.

Once she was settled, Raymond leaned over and kissed her gently on the forehead, whispering softly, "Everything will be okay. You're not going anywhere. Stop worrying so much and concentrate on getting better."

Tammy managed a little smile and nodded as she rested her tired body against the pillows. She had her doubts that they would remain together but was too exhausted to argue. Only time would tell, she thought.

CHAPTER 20

*U*nable to shake the huge void that had taken over her life since losing the baby, Tammy plummeted into a depressive rut. She mourned in bed for two days straight. Raymond tried persistently to raise her spirits with words of encouragement and affection, but all to no avail. Any hopes of their relationship returning to normal seemed like a distant dream.

During the first few days, words of anger and hate fired back and forth between them, only to be regretted soon after. Clinging to the belief that, over time, their passion would return, the anger began to subside and both made the attempt to be civil to one another, agreeing to work through the emotions as and when they arose.

By day four, Tammy was beginning to feel a little better. Physically, much of her strength had returned and her appetite was improving. Finally pulling herself out of her depressive state, she told Raymond of her plans as he served her coffee on the deck. "I think I should try calling my dad today," she said casually as he took a seat next to her. "It's been four days since he called. What do you think?"

Raymond didn't hesitate to answer. Even though there was no hope for him and John to reconcile, he desperately wanted to see Tammy and her father make amends. "I think it's a great idea. I have to go look at a job after this cup of coffee, so you'll have the whole place to yourself to talk to him."

Tammy shifted in her seat. "He actually wants me to speak to Joanne, but if he answers, then we'll be forced to speak to each other. I need him in my life. As nervous as I am, I hope he is able to forgive me."

Raymond reached over and stroked her hand. "I'm sure when he hears your voice, all will be forgiven."

After Raymond left, Tammy paced the living room until she finally felt she had the courage to call her father. Summoning all her strength, she marched over to the dining room table, picked up the phone, and dialed his number.

After five rings, Joanne answered the phone. Subconsciously, Tammy let out a sigh of relief.

"Hello, Joanne speaking."

"Hi, Joanne, it's Tammy. How are you?"

"Hey, Tammy, I'm good, how about yourself?"

"I'm good," Tammy lied. "Dad called here a few days ago. He mentioned something about immigration and asked if I would call you."

"Yes. Apparently, you have an interview with them in about a week and a half. Your father needs to go with you. Hold on a second, let me find the letter and give you the date and time."

Tammy heard a clunk as Joanne put down the phone.

A few minutes later, she came back on the line. Tammy could hear papers being ruffled. "Hi, Tammy, are you still there?"

"Yes I'm still here."

"I have the letter. It states your interview is in ten days at two o'clock in San Francisco. It's going to take you guys at least three hours to drive there. I'd be here at the house no later than ten in the morning," Joanne said.

"Wait. Just Dad and I are going?" Tammy questioned, feeling a rush of panic.

"Well, yes, Tammy. I have Andrew, so I can't go."

Tammy shuddered at the thought of the grueling three-hour car ride alone with her father. "Well, that's going to be awkward. I haven't spoken to him since I moved out. What am I supposed to say? Hi, Dad, I missed you," she said, sarcastically.

"Don't overthink it, Tammy. You'll be fine. It's probably just what you guys need, you know, to work things out with each other."

"I'm not sure. Dad's pretty stubborn. I hope you're right."

"I hope I am, too," Joanne replied, sighing. "Sorry, I have to go. I hear Andrew waking up. We'll see you next week. Remember, we love you."

"Love you, too. Bye," Tammy said before hanging up the phone.

Taking Joanne's advice, Tammy refused to dwell on the trip to San Francisco with her father. Instead, she focused all her energy on the interview and tried to prepare herself for possible questions they may ask. She couldn't believe that after almost a year of waiting, she may soon be granted a green card. A status that would open the door to many opportunities; learning to drive, getting a job, and buying a car were just a few that came to mind.

By the morning of the interview, she had all her immigration papers in order, including her passport and visa. She chose to wear a sophisticated black knee-length skirt and a white shirt with black pumps. She wore little makeup and a simple gold chain around her neck with a matching chain around her wrist.

Having still not spoken to her father, Tammy didn't want to make matters worse by having Raymond drive her to his house. The thought of them bumping into each other terrified her. So, to avoid any potential confrontations, she thought it would be best to walk there. A fight would be the last thing she needed on such an important day.

CHAPTER 21

*T*he walk to her father's house started out pleasant. She felt excited but nervous, and spent some much needed quiet time gathering her thoughts. It was almost springtime with no clouds in the sky, and the air was completely still. Trees were beginning to bud and traces of flowers were already blooming. But, as Tammy neared her father's house, her mood began to change. Dreading the moment she would be face to face with her father, she felt her heart racing against her chest and her palms were beginning to sweat. Unanswered questions were spinning around in her head. What would she say to him? How was he going to act toward her? Tammy hated to admit it but, at this moment, she felt petrified of her father for the first time.

As she approached the front door, Tammy took a deep breath and hesitated before knocking. She tapped the door three times and heard Joanne shout from inside. "It's open."

Tammy slowly opened the door, trying to ignore the fact that her palms were so moist that they just slid off the handle. Joanne was sitting at the dining room table with a cup of coffee and the newspaper, dressed in a casual navy blue sweat suit. Andrew sat next to her in his high chair eating Cheerios. He smiled at Tammy as she approached them.

"Hey, Tammy, you look nice. Want some coffee? Your dad is still upstairs."

"Sure, that would be great. Thanks," Tammy said as she took a seat next to Andrew while Joanne scurried off to the kitchen.

"How have you been?" Joanne asked, returning with coffee in hand.

Once again, Tammy had to lie. "Good. How about yourself?"

"Oh, fine. Your dad shouldn't be too much longer."

"I wish you were coming with us, Joanne."

"Why?"

"Because Dad is still mad at me and we haven't spoken since I moved out. It's going to be so uncomfortable riding with him in a car for three hours," Tammy said, shuddering.

Joanne chose her words carefully. She wanted Tammy to see the positive side of the situation. "Hon, it just might be what the two of you need. You'll be forced to talk to each other and hopefully work everything out so you can be father and daughter again. Sometimes, when you're forced into an uncomfortable situation, it makes you face your fears," Joanne said. She then added some humor in an attempt to lighten the mood. "The problem is, you and your father are too much alike. You're both stubborn."

Tammy managed a half-smile. "I know. It's just that Dad is so angry, and I don't know how to deal with him."

"Yes, he's angry, and I can't say I blame him. But the bottom line is, you're his daughter, no matter what, and he stills loves you very much."

"I know and I love him too. I just don't know how to deal with this ." Tammy paused "Any suggestions?"

"No, Tammy, I don't. When the time is right, you'll know what to say."

Hoping for more advice, Tammy was about to drill her with further questions when she heard footsteps descending the stairs.

"Shit! He's coming," Tammy said in a panic. Suddenly feeling awkward, Tammy stood to greet him, shifting on her feet, unsure of how to stand. Ignoring the sound of her pulse pounding in her ears, she waited in silence for her father to appear.

He paused at the bottom of the stairs, looking sharp in a gray suit and matching tie with a white shirt and shiny black dress shoes. Saying nothing, he gave Tammy a frigid stare.

Feeling herself shrink in size, Tammy was already finding the silence between them unbearable. To avoid his piercing stare, she turned to Andrew for a distraction.

Her father cleared his throat before speaking—something he has always done when he felt uncomfortable. "Are you ready to go?" he asked in a flat tone.

"Yes," Tammy answered.

For the first hour, they rode in silence. The tension between them was intense. Her father looked straight ahead at the road in front, oblivious to her presence. Tammy couldn't remember a time in her life when she had felt so disquieted. With her arms crossed and her head turned away, she stared out of her window, frozen, afraid to move or speak.

A feeling of defeat began to creep over Tammy as she realized she might be unable to fix her broken relationship with her father. Then, she remembered what Joanne had said to her; when the time is right, you'll know what to say. All she wanted was for her father to feel proud of her again. She missed the sparkle in his eyes and his smile when he saw her. She missed asking him for advice. She needed her father and desperately wanted him back in her life more than anything.

It was like a switch just went off in her head. Tammy finally understood. She said it to herself one more time; she missed having her father in her life more than anything—that was it! Why hadn't she thought of this before? She needed him much more than she needed Raymond. Tammy realized what she had to do. She knew how to get her father back. It all made sense now. She didn't want to think about whether she was doing the right thing or not; she wanted to act on it now before she lost her courage and gave in to her cowardice.

Smiling, Tammy sat up tall and turned to her father. "Dad, I want to come back home." She held her breath, anticipating his response.

To her dismay, he said nothing. Not even a flinch. He just stared at the road ahead.

"Dad, did you hear me?"

Rarely did her father show emotion, and she wasn't expecting anything different now, but she had hoped for something more than silence.

In his own callous way, not taking his eyes off the road, he finally spoke. "I heard you, Tammy, and I must say I'm pleased to hear you've come to your senses at last." With a slight turn of his head, he flashed a weak smile at her.

For Tammy, the subtle smile meant the world. She felt triumphant. It broke the barrier and put her at ease in an instant.

"I'm not going to ask any questions as to why you've decided to come home," he said. "I'm just happy to hear you are."

As Tammy predicted, her father was straight to the point. She knew he didn't need to hear the details of her relationship with Raymond—thank goodness. It was enough for him to know it was now over and they could begin picking up the pieces of their shattered relationship.

John's face gradually became alive again with brighter eyes and a placid grin. The tension between them had weakened. Tammy knew she had her father back and, for the first time in a long time, she knew she had made the right decision. As their journey progressed, so did their relationship. Conversations of Tammy's plans, if granted a green card, were discussed along with her father offering driving lessons and Tammy's enthusiasm to look for a job. By the time they reached San Francisco, Tammy was feeling more confident about their relationship. As the car came to a halt, she told him she would pack that night and move back home the next day.

Tammy spent two hours with the immigration officers. A grueling period of time spent going through various papers and answering a whole host of questions. When did she arrive? Where was she staying? Did she have any children? That question had been a tough one to answer. No wonder it had taken her so long to get an interview, she thought, if this is how much time they spent with each person trying to gain entry to the country. With the interrogation finally complete, she was overjoyed when the officer said she was going to be granted a green card. Now she could begin getting her life back on track.

On the way home, they stopped for dinner at a restaurant and were back in Lonesridge by early evening. Not wanting to risk spoiling her father's mood by asking him to drop her off at Raymond's, Tammy made the excuse that she had to go to the market and would be happy to walk home. Before exiting the car, she gave her father a light peck on the cheek. "I love you, Dad."

"I love you too, Tammy."

The words brought music to her ears. She never wanted to forget how good they made her feel. Right at that moment, she promised herself that she would never do anything to jeopardize her precious relationship with her father ever again.

CHAPTER 22

*W*alking up the silent, darkened driveway toward Raymond's house, Tammy felt confident in her decision and suffered no guilt about leaving him. After spending the day with her father, she knew she was doing the right thing. Joanne was right—that car ride was just what they'd needed.

As she approached the front door, she heard the TV blasting from inside. Letting herself in, Tammy found Raymond sitting in the lounge chair drinking a beer and looking overly relaxed watching a western. The smell of pot lingering in the air served as an explanation as to his placid state.

Hearing the door close, Raymond turned his head and greeted Tammy with a goofy grin—one that is only manageable after smoking marijuana. "Hey, Tammy, how'd it go?"

After tossing her purse on the table, she took a seat on the couch, lit a cigarette, and inhaled deeply before answering. "It went great. They granted me a green card, so I'm now officially a permanent resident of the United States of America!" she said, smiling.

In a toast, Raymond held up his beer. "That's fantastic!

Congratulations. Do you want a beer to celebrate?"

"No thanks." Stalling for a few seconds, Tammy took another hit off her cigarette. "Raymond, I've been thinking. I think it's best if I move back in with my dad."

Tammy waited for his reaction. He didn't seem upset or look like he wanted to argue with her. He simply nodded in agreement. "Well, if that's what you want, I can't stop you." He took a sip of his beer. "I guess you and your father are okay now?"

Thankful that Raymond wasn't making her decision difficult, Tammy felt at ease explaining her reasons for wanting to leave. "For the first hour, we didn't talk or even make eye contact. It was bloody awful. I hadn't realized how much I'd hurt him until we were alone in the car together. Seeing nothing but anger and shame in his eyes tore me apart. And then, it just hit me. As soon as I told him I wanted to come back home, we began talking again." Tammy drained the last of her cigarette and stubbed it out. "We both know it's over between us. It has been since I lost the baby. It's the only reason I moved in here, but when I did, it changed everything. It's just neither one of us wanted to admit it."

Without interrupting, Raymond nodded in silence. He knew she was right and admired her for being braver than he would have been if he were in her shoes. He was happy to hear that her and John were now speaking and picking up the pieces, but in the same breath, he knew his friendship with John could never be repaired. For that, he was deeply sorry.

Showing no hard feelings, Raymond gave Tammy a friendly smile. "You're right. Things have changed between us. I just didn't want to admit it. I do have to say, though, I'm going to miss you. I didn't think I could live with someone, but you proved me wrong. It's going to be awfully quiet around here." He took another sip of beer. "When do you plan on leaving?"

"To avoid any awkward moments, I thought about having Joanne pick me up tomorrow while you're at work. Is that okay with you?" Tammy asked.

"That's fine. I understand. I'm curious, though. Did your father say anything about me while you were with him?"

"No, he didn't, and I was afraid to mention your name. I was thrilled when we began talking again and didn't want to say anything to jeopardize it. I'm sorry our little fling cost you your friendship with my dad. Maybe, over time, you guys will be able to work things out."

Raymond shook his head. "I doubt it. I don't think he could ever look me in the face again without being reminded that I slept with his daughter. To be honest, if I were a father, I'd feel the same way. I could forgive her but not the guy. I'd always blame him for seducing my daughter. I can't say I blame your dad. He's acting like any father should."

"Do you want me to talk to him?" Tammy asked.

Her gesture surprised him. "Oh God, no. Just let it be. The damage is already done, but thanks for asking."

Tammy left the couch and walked over to her now ex-lover, still sitting in the chair. With a friendly smile, she leaned over and embraced him.

"No hard feelings?" she asked.

"None. I'm good. It was just a matter of time until this happened, and I'm fine with it."

"Thanks. Me too. I'd better go pack. I want to call Joanne early so I can spend the afternoon looking for a job."

"Wow, you're not messing around, are you?"

Tammy laughed. "Ha! I've been messing around since I got here, but in the wrong way."

Raymond chuckled at her joke and watched her as she headed toward the bedroom. No doubt he was going to miss her, but he was going to miss John's friendship even more. He had always thought very highly of the man and was proud to have called him a friend. Feeling disgraced with himself, he sunk lower into the chair and chugged down the rest of his beer.

CHAPTER 23

*I*t seemed life in the States was finally smoothing out for Tammy after her reckless beginnings with Raymond. It'd been a year since their break up. Having no regrets or remorse; she couldn't be happier. Still living with her father and Joanne, it felt good to have no secrets and to not have to constantly be telling lies. Raymond was a thing of the past. His name was never mentioned and sadly, her father never rekindled his friendship with him.

Occasionally, Tammy would bump into Raymond in town. Each time with a different woman on his arm. He seemed content to have his old life back. With no hard feelings, they would always take time to say hello and make small talk.

For Tammy and her father, it was like old times. Their relationship slowly repaired itself. Together, they discussed her plans and her father expressed his desire for her to go to college. Tammy had agreed, but she also confessed she wanted to postpone it for a while so she could look for work. It had been a long time since she had earned an income and she yearned for some independence.

Within two months of receiving her green card, Tammy had

passed her driver's test. It changed everything for her. Under the condition that she soon buy her own car, Tammy's father loaned her one of his. Being back on the open road gave Tammy the most freedom she had experienced since arriving in the States.

Wasting no time, Tammy found a job as a waitress at the local hotel. Her previous experience proved invaluable; it helped her secure the job with ease. She worked the lunch and dinner shifts five days a week. The money she earned was easy to save because she had no rent or bills to pay. So, within six weeks, she had managed to save five hundred dollars, which she used to buy her first car—a Mercury Zephyr.

That summer, much to everyone's surprise, Tammy's father kept his promise and invited Rose to the States for an all-expenses-paid, two-week visit. Having not seen her mother in almost two years, Tammy cherished every moment.

Joanne was the perfect host, insisting Rose stay at the house. At first, John had his concerns, but they soon subsided after observing the friendship that flourished between Joanne and his ex-wife. To his delight, everyone got along exceptionally well. During her mother's visit, Tammy took her on many day excursions, including the Gold Rush town—which stirred up memories of Raymond—San Francisco, and Yosemite.

Around the dinner table, serious discussions, stories, and fond memories of Donna were shared. The more time that elapsed with no news, the more they all began to fear the worst. With no leads or any word from the children's home, no one had any idea how to go about looking for her.

Not wanting to upset her mother even more, Tammy chose not to tell her about her relationship with Raymond or the miscarriage; there were some things she just didn't need to know.

The two weeks zipped by quicker than Tammy would've liked, and saying goodbye to her mother all over again was difficult. Many tears were shared at the airport and promises of writing were made by both Tammy and her mother. Tammy left with a heavy heart, not knowing when she would see her mother again.

Tammy had been working at the hotel for eight months, making new friends, and was now dating a chef called Steven. Being from a Spanish decent, his smooth skin always looked tanned. He was tall, over six feet, and lean but not muscular. His head of wavy black hair rested on his shoulders, and Tammy had been captivated from the first moment they met by his dark blue eyes, beautifully framed with thick black eyelashes. But it was his smile, topped with a black mustache that drew Tammy in and really melted her heart. He had passed her in the break room and their arms had brushed, which caused her to look up. He said nothing, but simply smiled, followed by a wink of the eye. Tammy smiled back and then he was gone.

The next day, she saw him again. This time, he spoke, introducing himself as Steven and showing off, once again, his heart-warming smile. Instantly, they struck up a friendship. Drinks were shared after work and days off were spent with each other. She grew fond of him quickly, and within a few months, their relationship had grown to the official "being a couple" stage.

Unable to afford his own place, Steven lived with one of his friends in a one-bedroom apartment across town where Steven slept on the couch. He didn't own a car, but Tammy's was at his disposable whenever he needed a ride. If she had to work, she simply loaned him the car.

One afternoon while Tammy was at work, Steven came into the kitchen to start his night shift. He seemed upset. Without giving her a glance, he mumbled a quick "Hi" before dashing over to his locker to put on his apron.

Concerned, Tammy set down the tray she was carrying and followed him. She found him at the lockers with his back toward her. "What's up? You look upset," she asked, gently placing her hand on his shoulder.

Still facing his locker and struggling with the strings on his apron, he eventually turned to face her. With a distressed look on his face, he yanked the ties one last time and pulled the ends into a tight knot around his middle. "Oh, well," Steven started in a raised voice, "my stupid roommate is kicking me out because his girlfriend is moving in." Frustrated, he slammed the metal locker door shut. "I have until the weekend to move out. Some *friend* he is! I can't afford a place of my own, so what am I supposed to do now? I'm really fucked!"

Clearly in a riled state, Steven brushed past Tammy, shoving her out of his way, and grabbed a metal chair out from under the staff table. Tammy covered her ears and winced at the high-pitched screech of metal legs scraping across the tiled floor. Steven flopped himself down on the seat with his folded arms on the table and his brows in a deep furrow.

Alarmed by his anger, Tammy cautiously took a seat next to him, placed her hand on his knee, and gave it a slight squeeze. "Is there anywhere else you could go?" she asked.

For the first time, Steven made eye contact. My god, he looks awful, Tammy thought. His dark, glazed eyes hooded by droopy eyelids made her shift awkwardly in her seat. The look on his face was one she'd never seen before.

In a calmer state, Steven leaned back in his chair and sighed. "I have another friend who is moving out of his place this weekend. I might be able to get that apartment, but I can't afford it on my own."

Tammy knew him well enough to know what he was getting at. "What are you saying? You want me to move in with you, is that it?" Steven took her hand. "It's crossed my mind, yes. But I have no idea how we're going to come up with the deposit. I'm broke until payday."

Tammy pondered the idea for a moment. The subject of becoming roommates had never been discussed before, but she understood Steven was desperate. Plus, the idea of not having to live with parents and having a place of her own was appealing.

"I'll be a good roommate. I promise," Steven said with a grin while batting his long eyelashes at her.

Tammy smirked. "Well, I do have the deposit. I don't pay rent at my dad's, so I'm able to save the money instead. And I have a car, so we'll have transportation. How much is the rent?"

"Five hundred," Steven replied.

"That's not too bad. We both work. I'm sure between us we could come up with that." A large grin blanketed Tammy's face. "So what do you think? Want to be roommates?"

"We're gonna need the first month's rent too. That's another five hundred," he said.

"Well, I've managed to save about two thousand dollars," Tammy said, beaming with excitement. She grabbed his arm, shaking it vigorously. "We have the money, Steven!"

Being unexpectedly surprised and gushing with relief, Steven shared in her giddiness. "You've been hiding out on me, babe! You have two thousand dollars!" he said, looking like the cat that got the cream. With his spirits now shifted into high gear, he reached over and threw his arms around Tammy, blubbering at speed. "Let's go talk to my buddy tomorrow and see how we can make this happen."

"Sure," Tammy answered, thrilled to see him happy again. "I get off at two tomorrow. We can go then if you like?"

"Sounds good to me. I'll call my friend and tell him we're coming over." He pulled her in closer and gave her a passionate kiss. "Thanks, babe. You're the best!"

Tammy smiled. "You're welcome."

"I can't believe we're getting our first place together. I'm so stoked!" With all the excitement, he realized he had lost track of time and glanced at his watch. "Oh, crap! I'd better go clock in. I'm late for my shift. I gotta run. Love you, babe."

"Love you too!" Tammy hollered as she watched him scurry away with a bounce in his step.

The pressures of the night—burned food, irate customers, and those that left no tip—couldn't dampen Tammy and Steven's elevated mood. They unashamedly shared their news with co-workers and Tammy couldn't wait to get home to tell her father and Joanne the unexpected but exciting plans.

~

H ome by nine, Tammy found her father and Joanne drinking wine and playing scrabble at the dining room table. "Hi, guys," she said cheerfully as she pulled off her coat by the door.

"Hi, Tammy, how was work?" Joanne asked, peering over her glasses.

Tammy threw her coat on the couch and walked over to the table. "It was good. Who's winning?" she asked while pulling out a chair and taking a seat.

"Joanne is. She must be cheating," her father joked.

Tammy laughed at his dry sense of humor. Pleased to find they were obviously in good spirits, Tammy wasted no time. "I don't mean to interrupt your game, but I have something to tell you."

Anticipating bad news, her parents quickly lost interest in the game and turned to Tammy with matching worried expressions. "What is it?" Joanne asked.

Tammy grinned. "Don't worry, it's nothing bad. Steven and I may be moving in together." Her father removed his glasses, leaned back in his chair, and folded his arms across his chest. A posture Tammy recognized well—this was his go-to look for when he wasn't pleased.

"Really. What brought this on?" he asked.

"Steven is getting kicked out of his apartment. Apparently, his roommate who leases the place wants his girlfriend to move in. Steven has another friend who's moving out of his apartment and Steven suggested we rent it. We're going to look at it tomorrow after work."

"I didn't know you and Steven were that serious," Joanne remarked.

"We're not. Heck, we've only been dating for about four months. The thing is, he can't afford the apartment on his own and I think it's about time I got my own place anyway," Tammy explained.

"Can you afford it?" questioned her father.

"I think so," Tammy replied. "We're both working and the rent is only five hundred a month, so I think we should be able to afford it between us." She decided not to disclose the fact that she was covering the security deposit and first month's rent. They would only dispute the idea and insist she just pay her half. She didn't want to explain that Steven had no money until his next paycheck.

Unsure on how to handle the sudden news, John glanced over at his wife for reinforcement. Showing no signs of objection, Joanne gave a slight nod and a smile. John replied with a subtle nod and turned to his daughter. Their silent communication never failed to amuse Tammy.

"Well, seems like you have it all figured out." John raised his glass in a toast. "I hope you get the apartment and I wish you guys the best of luck."

Tammy left her chair and walked over to her father. Leaning over the back of his seat, she hugged him around the neck. "Thanks, Dad. I'm pretty excited."

Joanne smiled from across the table. "If you get the apartment, I have extra dishes you can have and probably some extra bedding."

"Thanks, Joanne. That would be great. I know the place is furnished, but items like that we could really use."

After sharing the news with her parents and securing their blessings, Tammy couldn't wait to see the apartment. The idea of beginning a new life in a new place with Steven was exactly what she needed, and she failed to contain her elation as she skipped down the hall to her room.

CHAPTER 24

The next morning, Tammy woke up eager to see the apartment. With only fifteen minutes to spare before she had to leave for work, she decided to make a quick call to Steven to confirm the time.

She dialed his number and his roommate answered after a few rings. "Hello."

"Hi, it's Tammy. Is Steven there?" she asked.

"The lazy bum is still fucking sleeping," the roommate said with an attitude.

Never having met the guy, Tammy was shocked by his tone and rudeness. "Okay, well, could you please tell him I called and to not forget to meet me after work, to look at the apartment?"

The rude man let out a loud, crackling laugh. "You're shacking up with him?"

"Yes, I am. He told me you're kicking him out."

"Your damn right I'm kicking his ass out. Did he tell you why?"

"Yes, he did," Tammy replied.

"And you're still going to shack up with the guy?" He let out another contemptuous laugh. "You're stupider than he is."

Offended by his remark but rushed to get to work, Tammy had no time to play twenty questions. "Look, I have to go. Can you please just give him the message?" Tammy shook her head, baffled by the conversation, and hung up the phone. She grabbed her coat from the couch, yelled goodbye to Joanne upstairs and ran out the front door.

Shortly after two o'clock, Tammy spotted Steven at the staff table talking to another cook. She clocked out of her shift and walked over to him, stunned by his appearance as she approached the table. Wearing a pair of severely wrinkled black pants and an equally crinkled white t-shirt, Tammy assumed he had slept in them all night. His mangled hair splayed out over the top of his head in an uncombed mess, and he clearly hadn't taken the time to shave. When he looked up, she noticed his pale skin and the dark circles cradling his eyes.

"Steven, are you okay?" she asked.

"Yeah, why?"

"Well, you look like you've just crawled out of a bush."

Offended, he raised his voice. "What's that supposed to mean?"

Not wanting to upset him, Tammy refrained from commenting any further on his wardrobe malfunction. "Oh, never mind. When can we see the apartment?"

"My buddy will be home in about half an hour. His landlord is going to stop by too so he can meet us."

"Great! I'm so excited," she squealed before adding. "Um, can you at least brush your hair? We have to make a good impression, Steven."

"Jeez, Tammy! Don't worry. I'll brush it in the car."

Tammy's mood shifted to frustration. "Fine!" she snapped, rolling her eyes. "Wait here while I go cash in my tickets and collect my tips."

Thirty minutes later, they were pulling up to the parking lot of the apartment: A white two-story building with a dozen units overlooking the town. Tammy parked the car, rolled up her window and asked Steven to do the same, which he did after stubbing out his cigarette. Before exiting the car, Tammy glanced in the rear-view mirror, touched up her lipstick, and gave her hair a quick brush. Speaking only with her eyes—words were not needed—she handed the brush to Steven. Annoyed by her gesture, he rolled his eyes, snatched the brush from her hand, and obediently brushed his hair before stepping out of the car.

In silence, they walked up to the door marked 2A, which was located between two other apartments, and knocked on the door. A few moments later, a tall, skinny guy with short blond hair, still dressed in a brown company uniform, appeared from inside.

"Hey, Randy, how's it going? This is my girlfriend Tammy," Steven said while slinking his arm around her waist.

"Hi, Tammy, nice to meet you. Come on in," Randy said as he opened the door and took a step to the side.

"Nice to meet you, too," Tammy replied before following Steven into the apartment.

Inside, they found themselves standing in the living room. Randy closed the door behind them.

"May I look around?" Tammy asked.

"Sure," Randy said, sweeping his arms in a circular motion around the small space. "There's not much to see," he added.

Tammy left the two men to chatter while she went to explore, almost skipping from room to room with excitement. The apartment was small, with one bedroom and a tiny bathroom, but she was happy to see it at least had a bathtub and a shower. The kitchen was galley-style with a small nook off to the left for a dining room table. The living area, the biggest of the rooms, had two sliding glass doors leading out on to a deck with just enough room for two chairs. The awesome view from the deck overlooked the whole town, and Tammy was already picturing it as the perfect place for her morning coffee.

Tammy found Steven and Randy talking on the couch. "I love it!" she announced. "Did you take a look yet, Steven?"

"I've been here before. I don't need to," Steven replied, showing much less enthusiasm than Tammy.

"Randy, where's your landlord? I thought he was going to be here."

"He called just before you guys arrived. He'll be here in about ten minutes," Randy said.

"Okay, good. So, is any of the furniture included with the apartment?" Tammy asked.

"It comes with the fridge, cooker, couch, coffee table, and dining room table. The bed is mine."

"That's not a problem. I'm sure we can find a bed someplace for a reasonable price. Right, Steven?" Tammy added, hoping to include Steven in the conversation and perhaps encourage him to show a bit more interest.

Steven shrugged his shoulders and mumbled, "Yeah, I guess." Disappointed, Tammy walked away to check out the kitchen again.

A few minutes later, they heard a car pull up in the driveway.

"That must be the landlord," Randy announced.

Tammy stood by the dining room table, anxious to meet him. Moments later, there was a knock at the door.

"Come in. It's open," Randy yelled.

The door opened and a middle-aged man dressed casually in blue jeans and a grey sweatshirt entered the room carrying a manila envelope.

Tammy walked into the living room to greet him.

The landlord extended his hand and introduced himself. "Hi, I'm Bill. It's a pleasure to meet you both."

Tammy shook his hand first and was pleased when Steven stood to greet him. Doing most of the talking, Tammy and Bill walked through the apartment while she asked various questions. She asked if the utilities were included with the rent and was happy to hear they were. Correcting herself a few times for calling it a flat, Tammy was amused with Bill's sense of humor when he began calling it a flat, too. Eager to get the apartment, Tammy explained to Bill that her and Steven both worked and could easily afford the rent, adding for good measure that they had no children or pets.

Bill liked her spunk and enthusiasm and believed they would make good tenants. "Normally, I take applications and make my decision after viewing them. But, I like you, Tammy, so I tell you what," Bill said and paused.

Tammy took a deep breath as she waited. "What?" she finally asked after what felt like an eternity.

Bill smiled, enjoying her excitement. "If you have the deposit of five hundred dollars and the first month's rent, the place is yours."

Tammy held her hands together and squealed a high-pitched "Thank you!" to Bill before yelling, "Steven! We got it!" She raced toward the living room and saw Steven had returned to the couch. He couldn't help but cave in to her over-the-top excitement, and he stood to meet her in a triumphant hug.

After retrieving the necessary rental papers from his car, Bill ushered them both over to the dining room table to complete the process, go over the rental agreement, and answer any questions they may have. He informed them that it was a month-to-month lease and explained he would need a few days to clean and paint the place. He concluded they could move in next Monday, which was just four days away.

With no hesitation, Tammy signed the papers and then slid them across the table to Steven. While waiting for him to add his signature, Tammy pulled out her checkbook, wrote a check in the amount of one thousand dollars and handed it to Bill. Bill scanned the check, making sure everything was filled out correctly.

"Well, congratulations to the both of you," he said, extending his hand for another round of handshakes. Checking his watch, Bill slid the papers and check inside the manila envelope. "I'm sorry, but I have to get going. I have another meeting in half an hour."

Tammy and Steven followed suit as Bill stood up and walked to the front door. "Thank you so much, Bill. I can't tell you how happy you've made us." She took Bill's hand one last time. "We promise to take really good care of the place."

"Now, that's what I like to hear!" Bill said with a chuckle. "How about we meet here Monday morning at ten so I can give you the keys?"

"Sure, that sounds great!" Tammy answered.

After Bill had left and the door was closed, Tammy let out a loud triumph "Yes!" while pulling Steven into a victory dance. "I can't believe this place will be ours," she said, prancing around with joy.

Amused by her giddy antics, Steven twirled her in a spin and met her in a kiss. "Me neither, babe. I love you."

"I love you too, honey."

"Get a room, you two," chirped Randy from the couch.

Cheek to cheek, Tammy and Steven, snickered at Randy's remark.

"Thanks for everything, Randy," Tammy said before turning back to Steven. "Are you ready to go? I can't wait to tell my dad and Joanne that I finally have my own place!"

CHAPTER 25

*J*ohn and Joanne shared in Tammy's excitement over the apartment and, as promised, Joanne loaded her up with sheets, towels, dishes, and silverware.

The night before their big move, John invited Steven over to the house for dinner. Pleased that Steven had taken the time to at least shave, brush his hair, and put on some clean clothes, Tammy thought the evening had got off to a good start. Joanne had prepared spaghetti with garlic bread—one of Tammy's favorites— and John served everyone a glass of white wine with their meal.

Talk of the apartment ruled the table, with Joanne frequently asking if there was anything else they needed. Each time Tammy repeated her gratitude but assured her they were fine. John's primary concerns were their finances, wondering if they could afford the rent every month. Not wanting her father to worry, Tammy tried her best to put his mind at ease by going over what the two of them made each month. But, even after explaining everything more than once, her father still seemed unsettled. Tammy sensed something else was on his mind. Whatever it was, he didn't discuss it.

At the end of the evening, Tammy excused herself to grab a jacket from her bedroom so she could take Steven home. To Tammy's surprise, her father followed a few seconds later and closed the door behind them.

"Are you okay, Dad? What's up?" she asked.

Her father sat on the edge of the bed with his arms folded and a creased expression on his face. Knowing he rarely expressed his feelings, this was confirmation for Tammy that something was definitely troubling him.

"I'm not sure how to say this," he began. "I can't tell you what to do anymore...you're an adult. But I can still look out for you and, as your father, I'll never stop doing that."

"Where's this going, Dad?" Tammy asked, eager for him to get to the point.

"If you must know, it's Steven. I don't know him that well, and he does seem like a nice young man..."

"He is, Dad."

"Yes, I'm sure he is, but there's something about him that makes me uncomfortable. I can't quite put my finger on it. He hardly said a word all night and his behavioral pattern isn't consistent."

"What's that supposed to mean?" Tammy questioned.

"I have to ask...um, do you know if he's on drugs?"

Tammy was horrified. "What! Why would you ask such a thing? Of course he doesn't do drugs. Don't you think I would know, Dad?" Upset by her father's accusations, Tammy punched her arms through the sleeves of her jacket. "Are you being the over-protected dad? Maybe you think no one is good enough for me. Is that it?"

"I don't know. Maybe I am. But his behavior tonight struck me as odd. When he was sitting on the couch, he could barely keep his eyes open. Even when they were open, they weren't focused. It's like he was looking off into space or something."

Tammy thought her father's suspicions were nothing short of preposterous. "I promise you, Dad, he's not on drugs. Like I said, I would know. He's probably tired. I mean, he walked all the way here straight from work. I couldn't pick him up because I was helping Joanne with dinner."

John stood and gave his daughter's shoulder an affectionate pat. "I'm sure you're right, but I had my concerns so I had to ask. That's what fathers do. Anyway, I'll let you go so you can take him home."

Tammy smiled, relieved he didn't want to pursue the subject, and gave him a hug. "He really is a nice guy, Dad."

Her father nodded, but he wasn't convinced. He could only hope his suspicions were wrong.

CHAPTER 26

*a*fter picking up the keys from Bill, Tammy and Steven were settled in their new apartment within a few days. When it came time to buying a bed, a TV, and other miscellaneous items they needed, Steven confessed he had some unexpected expenses and was now broke. Refusing to wait another week until he got paid and wanting the apartment to be perfect, Tammy reluctantly spent more of her savings and bought the items herself.

Prior to the move, Tammy had suggested to Steven, to make finances easier, that he pay the rent every month and she would pay for everything else, which included the telephone, TV, food, toiletries, gas, and anything else they may need. Steven thought it was fair and agreed.

Over the next few months, their new life together got off to a great start. Tammy enjoyed having her independence back and making a home for them both, and she could finally invite some of her friends over for dinner. But, on several occasions, she found herself embarrassed by Steven's behavior. Glancing over at him while engaging in conversations with friends, she was horrified to find him in a vegetated state, his eyes closed and his head crouched low over the table. Oblivious to those around him, she watched in bewilderment as he mumbled and whispered random words or phrases to himself.

To save herself from any more embarrassment, Tammy would kick him hard on the shin from underneath the table to discreetly jolt him awake. She was often met with a cold, angry glare and creased brows as Steven snapped out of his dream world, to which she would often reply with a fierce stare of her own while fighting to keep her lips tightly closed for the sake of everyone present.

Tammy found herself defending him more and more, just like she had with her father. She always explained to their guests that Steven was probably tired from a hard day's work before quickly excusing him from the table. Tammy desperately wanted to believe this was the reason for his strange behavior. She'd put aside her father's suspicions when she confronted Steven the next morning, only to be swooned with profuse apologies and feelings of embarrassment in return. He promised it would never happen again.

Surprise by how much she enjoyed being a homemaker, Tammy loved spending her days off cleaning the apartment or trying out new recipes for future dinner parties.

Thankful that Steven had to work all day, she had plans to clean the entire apartment with no interruptions. As soon as he left, Tammy began her day's activities by tuning the radio to a country and western station and turning up the volume. After rolling up her sleeves and grabbing her caddy of supplies, she worked her way around each room, cleaning, sweeping, and polishing while singing and dancing to her heart's content.

Being the least favorite, she left the bathroom till last. Before attempting the dreaded task, she decided she needed to properly prepare for the occasion and searched for a pair of rubber gloves underneath the sink. Instead, in amongst the bottles of cleaning products and spare toiletries, she came across a folded brown paper bag. Tammy, given she had always been the curious type, immediately forgot about the gloves and sat on the edge of the tub to do some snooping. She carefully unfolded the bag, took a peek inside, and let out a loud gasp. Lying at the bottom of the bag, she found syringe needles, two teaspoons that were black on the bottom, and numerous small cotton balls. The only illness she associated with needles was diabetes. Having never known anyone with the condition, she had no idea what the blackened spoons or cotton balls might be needed for, but she found herself feeling pity for Steven.

"Oh my god," she whispered to herself. "Why didn't he tell me? Poor Steven, he didn't want me to know. I have to tell him it's okay and that I understand. He needs to know he doesn't have to hide it from me anymore." Feeling sympathetic, she carefully closed the bag and returned it to where she had found it under the sink.

Later that day, Steven arrived home in a seemingly flustered state. He threw his duffle bag on the couch and raced straight to the bathroom. Closing the door behind him, he hadn't even acknowledged Tammy, who had already served their dinner of roast chicken, mashed potatoes, and carrots. Offended, Tammy waited at the table with crossed arms and a furious stare as she watched the food she'd diligently cooked turn cold. Growing impatient, she yelled, "Steven, dinner's ready! What are you doing in there?"

From the bathroom, he shouted back, "I'll be right there. God, Tammy, I just got home! Give me a break, will you?"

Angered by his tone and tired of waiting, she proceeded to eat alone. Pausing with a mouthful of chicken, she soon came to the realization that he was probably taking his medicine. "How could I be so stupid?" she muttered under her breath. "He doesn't know I know." Now that she understood, she let her anger subside and prepared herself to tell him that she knew about his illness.

Ten minutes later, Steven exited the bathroom and joined her at the table. In silence, Tammy uncovered his dinner and slid the plate in front of him.

"Thank you," he said in a much nicer tone. "Are you feeling okay?" Tammy asked, trying to break the ice.

Without meeting her eyes, Steven replied, "Yeah, why?"

"Well, this morning, while I was cleaning the bathroom, I found a brown bag with some needles inside underneath the sink."

Steven froze. His body became tense and a look of fear flooded his face.

Tammy reached across the table and took his hand. "Why didn't you tell me?"

"Tell you what?" he asked, puzzled.

"That you're a diabetic."

Steven said nothing, which led Tammy to believe he was embarrassed. Comforting him, she rubbed the top of his hand with her thumb. "It's okay, Steven. It's nothing to be ashamed about."

Avoiding eye contact, Steven shifted his gaze downward and played along. "I didn't want you to feel sorry for me, and, um, I didn't want to bother you. I'm fine. It's no big deal."

Surprise by his modesty, Tammy let go of his hand. "Yes, it is a big deal, Steven. You're supposed to be watching your diet and sugar intake. Do you take insulin?"

"Can we just drop it? I'm okay and I know how to handle it."

Sensing his frustration, Tammy let it go, but she wondered why he'd never told her about his illness. It seemed she maybe didn't know him as well as she thought she did.

CHAPTER 27

The next morning, Tammy woke up experiencing severe back pain. Steven offered to take the day off and stay with her, but she ushered him off to work and told him she would be fine. Hobbling around the apartment, unable to stand up straight or walk comfortably, she was thankful she had cleaned the day before. Tammy discovered if she lay on the couch with a few pillows, the pain was slightly easier to deal with. Grateful for another day off, she spent most of it lounging in front of the TV, hoping her back would heal itself before she had to return to work.

By the time Steven returned home, Tammy was still lying on the sofa in excruciating pain.

"Hey, honey, how are you feeling?" he asked.

Groaning in agony, she slowly eased herself up to a sitting position. "Not much better, I'm afraid. I may have to call in sick tomorrow. I can't even stand, let alone work."

Concerned, Steven sat next to her on the edge of the couch. "Is there anything I can do?"

"Yes, can you rub my lower back for a bit? It's killing me," Tammy said, inching herself forward.

Hoping to ease her pain, Steven obliged.

"Maybe you should go to the doctors tomorrow," Steven suggested. "I have to work though. Will you be able to drive yourself there?"

"Yeah, I should be okay. It's only a few minutes down the road. I just want this bloody pain to go away. I've done nothing all day but lie on this stupid couch," she said, sounding frustrated. "You're going to have to fix yourself dinner. I can't move."

"Don't worry about dinner. I'll make you some soup and bring it to you."

Tammy had no objections to being waited on. With TV remote in hand, she slowly sank her body back down and rested her head on the pillows while Steven scurried off to the kitchen.

The following morning, feeling as stiff as a board and with her back showing no signs of improving, Tammy called in sick. Despite much resistance from Steven, she insisted he still go to work. As soon as he'd left for the day, she called her doctor and made an appointment for later that morning. Tammy then managed to take a shower, dress, and drive herself to the doctors, all the while struggling with her agonizing pain.

Sue, who often ate at the restaurant where Tammy worked, was at the front desk. "Hi, Sue, I have an appointment with Dr. Davis."

"Hey, Tammy, what's wrong with you?" Sue asked, noticing Tammy wincing as she stood by the desk.

"It's my back. I have this severe pain that won't go away."

"Hang on a second. I'll let the doctor know you're here," Sue replied before marching off through a door behind her.

Tammy decided she was more comfortable standing while she waited to be called. Happy to see no one else in the waiting room ahead of her, she assumed she wouldn't have to wait too long.

A few minutes later, Sue returned to her desk and flashed a

professional smile. "He can see you now, Tammy. It's the first door on the right."

"Thanks, I know the way," Tammy said, feeling relieved. She turned on her heel, albeit very gingerly, and slowly made her way to the double doors of the doctor's office.

She found Dr. Davis sitting on a low round stool with wheels, his back toward her, writing something in a file. She gently tapped on the opened door before entering.

The doctor turned his head and looked over his glasses at her. "Hi, Tammy. Come on in and have a seat on the examination table while I finish these notes. I'll be just a moment."

Not wanting to disturb him, Tammy gave a silent nod and perched as best she could on the edge of the table, letting her legs dangle over the side. She cupped her hands in her lap and waited. Scanning the room, she glanced at a poster on the wall displaying a detailed picture of the human skeleton. Squinting at the smaller poster next to it, she saw it was all about the three trimesters of pregnancy. Tammy gulped; haunted by the memories of the baby she had lost.

After a few moments, Dr. Davis closed the file and set it down on the table in front of him as he stood up to face Tammy. The almost miniature looking stool, now free from the doctor's weight, rattled halfway across the room on its rickety plastic wheels. The doctor smiled at Tammy as he removed his glasses, folded them, and put them in the top pocket of his white coat.

"So, Tammy, what seems to be the trouble?"

She held her side to ease the discomfort. "I'm not sure. I've had a severe pain in my lower back and sides for the last couple of days."

"Hmmm, okay. Let's take a look, shall we?"

Tammy sat up as straight as she could and lifted the back of her shirt. With cool hands, Dr. Davis pressed firmly on various muscles around her back and sides, periodically asking if she felt any pain. Tammy nodded with a yes when she did. After a few moments of poking and prodding, he pulled down her shirt back down and faced her. "Okay, I think you may have a kidney infection. A urine sample will tell me if I'm correct, so I'll send in Sue to take care of that."

"Okay," Tammy replied.

Dr. Davis then left the room, picking up Tammy's chart on his way out. Sue entered shortly after and handed her a plastic cup with a lid. "Here you go, Tammy. I just need a little bit. There's a small metal door in the wall of the bathroom where you can place the cup after you're done. And then just come back in here, okay?"

"Thanks, Sue," Tammy replied before heading to the bathroom. After following Sue's instructions and leaving her sample on the metal ledge, she headed back to the examination room to wait for Dr. Davis.

Tammy sat in silence for a further twenty minutes, which left her wishing she'd brought a book to read to help pass the time and keep her mind off the pain. Dr. Davis finally returned, carrying her file under his arm, and wheeled his wayward stool back to his desk before taking a seat. He retrieved his glasses from his top pocket, slid them on, and began to read her file. Tammy felt like another twenty minutes passed before he closed the file in his lap and glanced up at her over the top of his glasses.

"Well, Tammy, it seems you do have a kidney infection, which is quite common in an early pregnancy." .

"Early pregnancy?" Tammy asked, taking a few seconds to process what he'd said. "What are you talking about? I'm not pregnant."

"Indeed, you are, Tammy. I'm quite sure of it."

"But how can that be? I just had my period less than two weeks ago," she explained in an exasperated voice.

"Bleeding is not uncommon in the first trimester. But it's not your period. It's known as decidual bleeding and will probably stop before you enter the second trimester."

Puzzled, Tammy asked. "Decidual bleeding? What's that?"

"Basically, during the beginning of pregnancy, your body hormones can go a little haywire. This causes you to lose part of the lining of the uterus, which normally happens before the lining has completely attached itself to the placenta. It's not a health risk to you or the baby, and by all means, you should have a normal pregnancy," he said with an encouraging smile.

Unable to focus on the doctor's words, she only heard the word *pregnant* bellowing repeatedly in her head like a loud, beating drum. This was too much information for what she thought was going to be a routine doctor's visit to treat a simple case of back pain. She was in shock. Pregnant? She couldn't believe it. She had stopped taking the pill a few months ago because of terrible side effects and had planned on looking at alternative methods, but she had never gotten around to it with being so busy organizing their new apartment. She and Steven had been careful, she thought; but, obviously not careful enough.

"Tammy, are you listening to me?"

Tammy shook her head, forcing herself back to reality. "Er, yes, Doctor. Sorry."

"That's okay. I'm sure this is quite a surprise for you. I'm going to give you some antibiotics for the kidney infection. They're safe to take while pregnant. I'm also going to make an appointment for you at the hospital, for an ultrasound so we can find out just how far along you are."

Tammy gave him an almost imperceptible nod. "Okay, that sounds fine."

With nothing more to be said, Dr. Davis wrote her a prescription and set up an appointment for her in a couple of days at the hospital. After thanking him, she stood up, shook his hand, and left the room.

Back in her car, still shocked by the news, Tammy tried to grasp the notion that she was once again pregnant. She made a promise, right there and then, to love and nourish the baby while it grew inside of her. She wasn't going to let her body reject another child. The initial shock was beginning to wear off, and thoughts of having a child with Steven actually made Tammy smile. They had been dating for some time, and he had expressed that he wanted kids someday. Well, that "someday" was here already; it was here now! As she started up the car, she found herself feeling excited about telling him the news.

CHAPTER 28

Steven arrived home shortly after six, looking tired and flustered. Tammy couldn't help noticing the beads of sweat forming on his forehead, his drenched hair, and his dark, sunken eyes. "Are you feeling okay?" she asked.

"Yes, I'm fine!" he snapped, throwing his duffle bag on the couch and pushing past her. "I'll just be a minute," he called out as he scurried into the bathroom, closing the door behind him.

Tammy had seen the same routine every night and knew he would be at least fifteen minutes. They had never discussed it, but she suspected he was taking his diabetic medicine. It troubled her that he was still embarrassed about it and continued to hide it from her.

While he was in the bathroom, Tammy racked her brain, thinking how she was going to tell him about the baby. With the antibiotics kicking in and her back feeling a little better, she had managed to cook a special roast beef dinner, along with roast potatoes and steamed mixed vegetables. The aroma of the delicious meal lingered throughout the apartment. The only thing left to do was set the table, so she began the task while waiting for Steven.

Nervous about his reaction toward the baby, Tammy had a strong urge for a cigarette. She took a few long, deep breaths to help subside the cravings, determined to conquer her addiction, especially now that she was responsible for the health of their child.

After setting the table, Tammy stood back and admired her work. "Not bad," she said to herself. Along with the polished silverware and folded beige napkins, she had finished the table off with two pillar candles and a vase of fresh daffodils. She joyfully skipped back to the kitchen, humming a pleasant tune, and proceeded to bring out the main course, followed by the vegetables and two glasses of milk. No more wine, she told herself while setting down the drinks.

As she made herself comfortable at the table, she heard the bathroom door open. "Hey, honey, dinner's ready!" she hollered in his direction.

"Be right there."

She heard Steven rummaging about in the bedroom and assumed he was changing out of his work clothes. Now wearing black jeans and a t-shirt, Steven made his way into the dining room and sat down. Tammy admired him from across the table. He was no longer sweating, his eyes were brighter, and he had combed his hair away from his face. Smelling the scent of his freshly applied cologne as it drifted in her direction, she smiled. "You look good."

"Thanks, babe," he replied. Steven's eyes shined with delight as he took in the sight of the feast before him. "Wow! Looks like you're feeling better. What's the occasion?"

Tammy smirked. "I'll tell you over dinner. Come on; let's eat. It's getting cold."

"Okay," he agreed. Anxious to dig in, Steven began carving the roast. "Hey, how did it go at the doctors today?"

She decided to tell him the easy part first. "It turns out I have a kidney infection. The doctor put me on antibiotics."

"Damn...it's a good job you went then!"

Picking up his knife and fork, Steven scanned the table one more time, taking in the lit candles and the neatly folded napkins. "So why the fancy dinner?" he asked with a devious smile.

Feeling the butterflies in her stomach begin to stir, Tammy took a deep breath and laid down her silverware. The moment she had been anticipating for most of the day had finally arrived. "Well, the doctor did tell me something else."

A worried look blanketed Steven's face. "Is it serious?"

Tammy smirked. "That all depends on how you look at it." She looked straight into his eyes with anticipation. "Steven, I'm pregnant." A huge sigh of relief rushed from her lungs as soon as the words left her mouth. She had told him. Sitting motionless, she waited for his reaction.

Steven stared across the table at her in disbelief, his eyes like those of a deer's caught in the headlights of an oncoming vehicle. Seconds later, the huge smile that lit up his face put Tammy at complete ease. Giggling with joy, she watched with amusement as he lifted one hand over his racing heart while the other covered his gaping mouth.

Flustered with excitement, Steven scurried over to her side of the table, knocking his chair over in the process. Glancing down at her, he thought to himself how beautiful she was and how lucky he was to have her in his life. Straining her neck, Tammy looked up to him with a beaming smile. Steven leaned in closer and met her with a passionate kiss. A passion they hadn't shared for quite some time. Cupping her face with the palms of his hands, Steven gazed into her eyes, which were now shining with tears of happiness. "Are you serious? We're going to have a baby?" he said before releasing a scream of pure joy.

Tammy reached for his hand and squeezed it tight. "Yes, I'm serious, and I've been terrified all day about telling you. I wasn't sure how you were going to react or if you'd be okay with having a child."

"Okay with it? Tammy, I'm over the moon!" He wiped away a tear that was now rolling down her cheek. "We're going to have a baby! Oh, sweetheart, I couldn't be any happier. I love you so much and I'm going to be a great dad. You watch."

"I know you'll be a good father. Our baby is counting on it. Now, come on, let's eat before it goes cold."

Affections were high during dinner. Steven moved his chair closer to Tammy's and smothered her with kisses and cuddles while they shared in their joy of becoming parents. Tammy filled him in on the need for an ultrasound to determine her due date and together they pondered over the sex of the baby, possible baby names, and discussed when and how they would tell their parents.

Tammy had never felt closer to him. For the rest of the night, he was clearly ecstatic about the thought of being a father and a joy to be around. They laughed, they cuddled, and they smooched on the couch while watching a romantic comedy before ending the night with amazing sex. Finally, life was good. The thought that they were going to be a happy family made Tammy smile.

CHAPTER 29

*T*he next morning, still riddled with excitement, Tammy couldn't wait to call her father and Joanne and also her mother in England about her pregnancy. Even though she was feeling skeptical about her father's reaction, she was too exhilarated to worry.

After spending most of the morning on the telephone with family, Tammy finally hung up the phone after talking with her mother, who was overjoyed at the thought of becoming a grandmother for the first time and promised to find a way to come visit if her father couldn't help.

Joanne seemed genuinely happy, and she wasted no time in offering Tammy the heaps of clothes that Andrew had outgrown if the baby was going to be a boy. Her father had cordially congratulated her when he came to the phone after Joanne. Tammy had a hard time detecting any sincere excitement from him. She knew he'd always had greater plans for her, and having a child in her early twenties wasn't one of them.

Tammy had yet to meet Steven's mother, who lived alone in the suburbs of Los Angeles. Steven rarely talked about her but told

Tammy she was widowed at an early age because of his dad's alcohol addiction. She never remarried and raised Steven, their only child, alone. The few memories Steven had of his father were not pleasant. Visions of his parents yelling and screaming, followed by scenes of violence and rage, haunted him. His mother had become a recluse lost soul with no friends, spending her days in front of the TV watching soap operas and living off disability checks. Once out of the toxic household, he began a troubled life of his own. Steven had distanced himself from his mother and only called home on the holidays. He had, however, made the effort to call her and tell her about the baby. The conversation was brief, and whether he believed himself or not, he told her they would get down there to visit once the baby had arrived.

The following morning, Tammy was scheduled for an eleven o'clock appointment to have an ultrasound at the local hospital. Steven had switched his shifts so he could go with her. He dressed casually for the occasion, and Tammy, knowing she would have to change into a gown at the hospital, chose to wear loose fitting sweats and a sweatshirt.

With one hand on the steering wheel and the other tightly holding Tammy's hand, Steven drove to the hospital. Baby related chatter and laughter filled the car for the entire journey, with speculation of the due date and the sex of the baby fast becoming a fun guessing game.

When they arrived, they checked in at the reception desk and were told it would be about a fifteen-minute wait. Taking Tammy's hand, Steven led the way to a couple of empty plastic blue seats against the wall in the waiting area. Once seated, Tammy scanned the room, pleased to see it wasn't busy. An elderly man sat alone in the corner, his head buried low, reading a newspaper. A woman, about the same age as Tammy and very pregnant, sat across from them, holding her partner's hand with one hand and rubbing her large round belly with the other. She looked tired, wearing a loose fitting blue smock and sandals. Picturing herself that far along,

Tammy nudged Steven's arm with her elbow. Giggling, she whispered in his ear, "Look, that'll be me in a few months."

He quietly chuckled and leaned over to kiss the top of her head. "I can't wait, babe."

Still whispering, she replied, "Me neither." Feeling extremely happy and content with their lives, Tammy rested her head on his shoulder.

"Hi, are you Tammy Mellows?" asked a young nurse holding a clipboard.

Tammy raised her head to where the nurse stood at her side, sat up straight and smiled. "Yes, I am, and this is my boyfriend, Steven." The nurse shook Steven's hand. "Hi, Steven," she said, smiling warmly. "Will you both follow me?"

"Sure," Tammy answered.

Already on his feet, Steven took Tammy's hand and followed the nurse down the hallway. Midway down the hall, the nurse opened a door on their left and led them in to a room before closing the door softly behind them and walking to a desk along the back wall.

Feeling awkward and not knowing where to sit or what to do next, Tammy and Steven remained standing and nervously waited for instructions. The nurse pulled out a white gown from a drawer underneath the desk and turned to face Tammy.

"Tammy, I need you to get undressed and put this gown on. Make sure the opening is in front. The doctor will be in shortly, okay?"

Placing her purse on the floor in a corner, Tammy took the gown. "Okay, thank you," she replied.

Tammy started to undress as soon as the nurse left the room. "Steven, why am I so nervous? This is just a normal procedure to see how far along I am."

"It's okay," Steven replied. "I think hospitals make most people nervous, no matter what they're here for. Now, come on, let's get you in that gown before the doctor gets here."

Tammy chuckled and handed Steven her clothes as she removed them before slipping into the gown. Amused by the loose-fitting garment that hung well below her knees, Tammy pranced around the room with one hand on her hip, mimicking a model on a catwalk.

"Come on, silly, stop messing around. Let's get you up on the bed. The doctor's gonna be here soon!" Steven said while guiding Tammy in the direction of the exam table.

"Okayyyyy," Tammy answered playfully as she scurried over to the table and hoisted herself up. Steven assisted the best he could by arranging the single pillow behind her back and settling her against it.

Scanning the room, Tammy pointed to a monitor on her left. "Look! That must be where we will get to see the baby. I'm so excited!" she squealed. "This makes everything feel so real. Can you believe this is actually happening to us?"

Standing beside her, Steven lifted her hand up to his lips and placed a gentle kiss on the tips of her fingers. "I sure can now, being in this room."

A few minutes later, a light tap on the door interrupted their idle chat. "Come in," Tammy said. She propped herself up on her elbows and stared in the direction of the door as it opened.

A striking, tall brunette woman wearing a white overcoat entered the room. "Hi, I'm Doctor Leon. I'll be doing the ultrasound this morning," she said as she walked over to Tammy and shook her hand.

"Hi, Doctor, this is my boyfriend Steven," Tammy replied. "Hi, Steven. This must be a pretty exciting time for you both?"

"It sure is," Steven said, flashing a smile at Tammy.

Dr. Leon continued to chat while preparing the equipment next to the exam table. "So, Tammy, how have you been feeling? Any nausea? Weakness or headaches?"

"No, nothing. I feel great."

"Well, that's good to hear. This is a simple procedure and it won't harm you or the baby. We basically want to get an idea of how far along you are. Unfortunately, it will be too early to determine the sex of the baby."

"Okay." Tammy nodded, feeling more at ease by the soothing tone of the doctor's voice.

"Okay, Tammy, before we begin, I want to take your blood pressure. Can you put your left arm straight out for me?"

Tammy watched in silence as the doctor wrapped a black band around the top of her arm. After a few moments, Dr. Leon released the strap. "Good. Your blood pressure is normal. Shall we get started?"

"I'm ready," Tammy replied.

"Now, I want you to lie back and relax. I'm going to put some gel on your stomach that may feel a little cold. It just helps to get a better reading from the transducer."

As she lay back, Tammy glanced over at Steven and smiled. Together, they watched as Dr. Leon folded the gown away from Tammy's stomach and applied the gel. "Oh, you're right, that does feel cold," Tammy said with a giggle.

"Now, you're going to feel a slight pressure while I move the transducer around. The image will appear on the screen next to you."

Both she and Steven waited with anticipation as Dr. Leon began to move the transducer slowly over Tammy's stomach. Looking closely at the screen, the doctor paused. "Ahh, here we go," she said, smiling.

Tammy gasped. "Do you see it?"

"Yes. Here, let me show you." Dr. Leon reached over to the black and white screen and circled the outline of the fetus with her finger. "See, here's the head and here's the body, and you can clearly see the arms and feet." Dr. Leon circled another part of the screen. "And here you can see its nose and ears are beginning to develop."

With squinted eyes, Tammy and Steven leaned in closer to the screen, desperately wanting to see what the doctor was looking at. A confused look between them confirmed they just weren't seeing it.

Then, suddenly, Tammy squealed. "I see it! I see it!" She shook Steven's arm. "Steven, look! It's our baby. Oh, my gosh, that is the most beautiful thing I've ever seen." Shocked by what she was witnessing—her baby growing inside of her—Tammy cupped her cheeks in her hands as tears trickled down freely over her fingers.

With shadowed, teary eyes, Dr. Leon smiled at Tammy's excitement. No matter how many times she witnessed this moment of parents seeing their child for the first time on the screen, it always brought tears to her eyes.

Still struggling to see the image, Steven was now bent over at a strange angle right in front of the screen. He was trying his hardest to see what Tammy was pointing at with her finger. The fact that she was still shaking his arm wasn't helping him focus on the tiny image.

"Look, Steven, there it is! Oh, God, tell me you see it. It's our baby, Steven." She paused to wipe away more tears and then spoke softly to her child. "Hi, baby, it's your mommy and daddy. We can't wait to meet you and hold you, sweetheart. We love you."

"Oh my god, Tammy! I see it," Steven shouted at the top of his voice. "I do, look...there's it's foot," he yelled while outlining it with his finger. "Oh, wow, that's amazing." Still mesmerized by what he was seeing on the screen, Steven took in every detail of his child in silence. It hit him like a ton of bricks; it suddenly became undeniable—he was going to be a dad. At that precise moment, he knew he had to change his life around or suffer the consequences of losing his family.

Dr. Leon walked around to the front of the screen, interrupting Steven's thoughts. He squeezed Tammy's hand as the doctor spoke. "It looks like the baby is developing just fine, and from the size of the fetus, I would estimate that you're about three months along, which gives you a due date around the end of November or early December."

Tammy calculated the time in her head. "Wow! That's only six months away."

"Yes, it is," the doctor replied. "Now, let's listen to the heartbeat to make sure it sounds okay and there are no abnormalities."

Experiencing a love she'd never experienced before—the love between a mother and child—fear suddenly consumed Tammy. "Okay."

Strung with nerves, Tammy and Steven anxiously watched Dr. Leon prepare the equipment to listen to the heartbeat. Holding her breath, Tammy closely watched the doctor's face while she listened to the heart of the baby with some kind of fancy monitor. After a few moments, she smiled and removed the earpiece. "Everything sounds fine. The baby has a nice strong heartbeat, and it is beating normally."

Tammy let out a huge sigh of relief.

"Do you want to hear it?" the doctor asked.

Tammy's face lit up. "Can we?" she turned to Steven and beamed a radiant smile. Steven smiled back at Tammy—both stunned that they were about to hear the heartbeat of their unborn child for the first time.

"Sure. Just be real quiet so we can hear it, okay?" Dr. Leon instructed.

In silence, Tammy and Steven gripped onto each other's hands, anxiously waiting for the sound of their baby's heartbeat to come through the speakers. Seconds later, they heard the soothing, rhythmic beat of its tiny little heart. Sobbing tears of joy, Tammy held her hand up to her chest as she heard the magical sound of her child, alive and well, inside of her. It sounded healthy, just like the doctor had said. "Honey, do you hear that?" she whispered softly to Steven.

"I do, babe. I can't believe it." He leaned over and kissed the top of her head. "I love you so much."

"I love you too, Steven. We're going to be good parents, aren't we?"

"The best. I won't let you down, I promise."

Dr. Leon turned down the sound and smiled. "So, how was that?"

"Thank you, Doctor. That was awesome. It seems so real now. There's actually a baby growing in here," Tammy said, pointing to her stomach. She wiped her eyes with a tissue that Steven handed to her.

"Yes, there is. Which means you must take care of yourself. Watch what you eat, exercise daily, and get plenty of rest." The doctor turned, picked up the clipboard from the counter, and glanced over Tammy's chart. "You're scheduled to see Dr. Davis in a month. Until then, just take care of yourself and the baby. Okay?"

"Oh, I will, Doctor," Tammy said, rubbing her stomach.

"Okay then, I'll let you get dressed, and good luck with everything," the doctor said as she reached over and shook both their hands before exiting the room.

As soon as they were alone, Steven hurried toward the door. "Hey, Tammy, I have to use the bathroom really bad. I'll let you get dressed. Meet me in the lobby when you're done, okay?" he said, bouncing up and down on the spot in the partly open doorway.

"Sure, that's fine," Tammy replied, giggling at his display of desperation to get to the bathroom. Really, deep down, she was feeling disappointed. She'd hoped they would be able to discuss the magical moment they'd just shared together. But she didn't want to spoil the moment by protesting against his leaving, so she simply smiled and waved him on his way.

Pacing the lobby while waiting for Steven to return, Tammy found herself growing impatient. She glanced down at her watch; he had been gone almost twenty minutes. "What could be taking him so long?" she mumbled under her breath. Tired of waiting, she decided to go look for him. Just as she turned to head for the bathroom, she spotted him trotting down the corridor toward her.

Frustrated from all the waiting, she spoke with a sharp tone. "Did you get lost or something? You've been gone for almost half an hour."

"Jeez! Sorry, when you gotta go, you gotta go. I didn't know I had a time limit," Steven replied with a smirk.

With narrowed eyes, Tammy looked at him suspiciously. He seemed different. She couldn't quite put a finger on it. He was acting cocky and rude and his face was smothered with that horrible grin she'd grown to detest. She'd seen this side of him before and had questioned it then, too. Why had his mannerisms suddenly changed? She didn't have answers then, and she had no answers now. "I'm not going to argue with you, Steven. Let's just go. I have to drop you off at work." Tammy turned toward the exit and picked up her pace, leaving Steven to follow behind.

Five minutes into the ride, Tammy turned to him to say something and was surprised to find him sleeping. She nudged his arm. "Hey, are you okay?" Steven didn't stir. Raising her voice slightly, Tammy nudged his arm again. "Steven...wake up!"

Startling Tammy, Steven bolted into an upright position, his upper body standing to attention as he shook his head from side to side and blinked his eyes rapidly before rubbing them with his palms. "What? What! I'm fine!"

"You were sleeping."

"Jeez, isn't a guy allowed to sleep?" he said in the same annoying, cocky voice he used at the hospital. "Must be from all the excitement of today."

"You don't see me falling asleep, do you?"

"Get off my fucking case, Tammy. Okay?" Steven snarled.

God, I'm sorry! No need to bite my head off. This is supposed to be a happy time for us. Why the fuck are we fighting?"

"Look, I'm sorry. I just have a lot on my mind right now," he told her as she pulled up to the back door of the restaurant and yanked the car into park. Without any further explanations or words of apology, Steven flung open the car door and stepped out.

He leaned his head down into the open doorway to face her. "I gotta go. I'll see you tonight, okay?"

"Yeah, okay. Bye." Tammy answered in a flat, emotionless voice and waited for him to close the door.

After dropping Steven off, Tammy decided to go straight home and call her dad and Joanne about the ultrasound. She parked her car in her assigned parking space, grabbed her purse, locked the car door, and walked toward her apartment. From a distance, she noticed there was a note pinned to her front door. Thinking it might be a congratulations note from a friend on the baby, Tammy quickened her pace to read the joyous message. But, to her horror, it was nothing of the kind—it was an eviction notice for non-payment of rent. "What the fuck!" she yelled.

CHAPTER 30

$\mathcal{U}$sing one hand, she ripped the notice from the door and read it while her hands shook with anger and confusion. In bold red letters, the words "Eviction Notice" jumped out at her. Wondering how many other tenants had seen the notice, she felt her cheeks flush with embarrassment at the thought. "This has to be a mistake?" she said in a panic while fumbling with her apartment key. After several attempts, she managed to unlock the door and quickly rushed inside, slamming the door behind her. Needing answers, she threw her purse on the couch and immediately hurried over to the phone to call the landlord.

While the phone rang, Tammy tried to calm her heavy breathing. After four rings, Bill answered. "Hello. Bill speaking."

"Hi, Bill, it's Tammy Mellows from apartment 2A. I just found an eviction notice on my front door. Surely there must be some sort of mistake?" she asked, trying not to sound too desperate.

"I can assure you there's no mistake." His tone was sharp and unfriendly. "I've not received any rent from you two since you moved in. I've left phone messages and previous notices on your door but still no payment. I rented the apartment to you on good faith without running any background checks. Now I see that I was a fool. I'll never do that again, that's for sure!"

Shocked by what Bill was telling her, Tammy intervened. "Bill, I swear I had no idea. Steven was supposed to be paying the rent and I assumed he was."

"What about all the previous phone messages and notices I've left? Are you telling me you never received any of them?"

Tammy was becoming frantic. "No, I haven't, I promise. You must believe me," she begged. Suddenly, Tammy had a horrifying thought. Steven must have found the notices and hidden them from her or thrown them away. He must have erased the phone messages too. How could he? Why hasn't he been paying the rent? She didn't understand. "I'll talk to him, Bill. I'll see what we can do."

"No, I'm sorry, Tammy. Enough is enough. I want you both out by the end of the month, which is in just less than two weeks' time. I'm not sure if you're telling me the truth about not knowing anything, but if you are, you need to talk to that boyfriend of yours."

"Please, Bill, I'm having a baby. Can't we work something out? I swear I knew nothing about this." Tammy could hear the desperation in her voice as she continued to plead with him.

"No, I'm sorry, I can't. Please be out by the end of the month. I have to go now," he said, not an ounce of empathy in his voice. He hung up, leaving nothing but silence on the other end of the line.

Tammy was shaking in shock and disbelief. Still clinging to the phone, using the wall as a brace, she slid down on her knees and wept. An hour ago, she'd been on top of the world, feeling elated about the baby and becoming a real family with Steven. Now she felt like she didn't even know him. How could he be so deceitful? It was quite obvious he'd purposely been hiding the landlord's notices and keeping the phone message from her so she wouldn't know he hadn't been paying the rent. Missing a month's rent, she could understand, but they've been in the apartment for three months and Bill swore Steven hadn't paid anything. What was he doing with all his money? It made no sense.

Startled by the loud beeping noises coming from the phone, she realized she'd forgotten to hang it up. Pulling herself up off her knees, she placed the phone back on the cradle and wiped her eyes with her sleeve. She didn't know what was going to happen now. Where would they go? She needed answers from Steven. How could he justify not paying the rent? What was more important to him than their home?

With her head in turmoil, Tammy lulled around the apartment for the rest of the day trying to make sense of it all, but she came up empty. Unable to rationalize Steven's actions, her anger bubbled away inside of her as the day wore on.

Steven finally returned home after ten that evening. Having had all day to stew over her discoveries, Tammy's anger had reached boiling point. With a piercing stare and a frown of disapproval, she glared at him from the couch when he walked through the door. No words were needed to express her apparent fury. Her stony silence, folded arms, and crossed legs were more than enough to convey her feelings.

Steven was in no state to question her about her foul mood. With his hands shaking and sweat beginning to form on his forehead, he needed to take care of himself first. "Hey, babe, I'll be right there. I have to use the bathroom," he said as he scurried past Tammy, careful to avoid any kind of eye contact.

"Fine," Tammy replied in a stern voice, now refusing to so much as even look in his direction.

Fifteen minutes later, he finally emerged. Tammy hadn't shifted from her seat, and Steven approached her with caution, feeling all too aware of the tension between them.

His attention was drawn to a piece of paper lying on the coffee table in front of her. He instantly recognized it as an eviction notice, just like the other three he had torn down from the door and destroyed. "Oh crap...I-I can explain," he blurted out in a breath of hurried stutters. Really, he had no idea what he was going to say next. He couldn't tell her the truth. She just wouldn't understand.

Tammy remained seated with her arms still folded as she leaned back and gave him another piercing stare. "How are you going to explain not paying our rent for three months?" she yelled in a high- pitched voice. "What the fuck was you thinking? Do you know how embarrassing this is for me?"

Unable to look at her, Steven glanced at the floor and sat beside her with a forlorn look. He reached for her hand. "I'm sorry."

Tammy smacked his hand away with a harsh swing and stood up. Enraged, she placed her hands on her hips and began pacing the room. "Where the hell did all your money go, Steven? The only thing you had to pay was the rent. I pay for everything else. How could you be so goddamn irresponsible?"

Steven shrugged his shoulders. "I don't know. It kind of just went."

"On *what* for God's sake?" she screamed, fast losing her patience with his lame excuses. The thought of having to look at him made her stomach churn. She despised him. All this time he had kept this from her. How could he? What was going to happen now? She certainly didn't have three months' rent, and neither did he—obviously. "Answer me! It went on WHAT Steven? You haven't brought anything home that costs nearly as much as even one month's rent."

"I don't know, just stuff," he mumbled, shrugging his shoulders.

"Stuff? What the...I don't get it! How did you not pay our rent? Did you just decide you couldn't be bothered? Did you forget?"

Steven was still looking at the floor and simply shrugged his shoulders again.

"What the hell are we supposed to do now, Steven? Oh yes, I talked to Bill, and guess what? He wants us out by the end of the month. Do you have any idea where we'll go when we're homeless, hmm?" Tammy knew he didn't have any answers. At a loss, she stood in the middle of the room and covered her face, allowing the pent-up frustrations of the day to drain away as she wept into her trembling hands.

Steven knew he had to fix the mess he'd created. This was their first major argument, and he couldn't stand seeing her so upset. He'd planned to catch up with the rent before she found out, but the months and the paychecks came and went so quickly; he just couldn't do it. Knowing he had to do something to comfort Tammy, he raised himself off the couch, walked over to her, and placed his hand gently on her shoulder. "I'm really sorry," he said, his voice riddled with apprehension. "I thought I would be able to get caught up. I swear."

"Don't touch me!" Tammy yelled, shoving him away. "How could you do this?"

Steven approached her again, with a little more caution this time, and attempted to embrace the mother of his unborn child. "Shh, it's going to be okay."

This time, Tammy didn't push him away. She felt herself weakening and melting into his touch. He sounded sincere and genuinely sorry for what he'd done. She relaxed her body and nuzzled her face into his chest as she continued to cry.

"Let me make some phone calls," Steven said, stroking the back of her hair. "I'll see what I can come up with, okay? I'll take care of this, I promise."

She looked up at him, her eyes now swollen and red, her nose running onto her sleeve. "Who are you going to call, Steven? I'm scared. We have nowhere to go and we're having a baby," she mumbled in between sniffs.

He held her face in his hands, gently kissed her on the lips, and brushed away the tears from her cheeks. "I'll think of something, okay? Just leave it to me. I fucked up but I'll fix it. Trust me."

She'd already trusted him to pay the rent in the first place and he'd failed. Could she trust him again? Tammy didn't know. But, right at that moment, she felt she had no other choice.

CHAPTER 31

Trying to keep her stress under wraps while at work or visiting her parents was becoming a challenge for Tammy. As the end of the week drew near, panic was beginning to set in. Steven still hadn't come up with a solution. On the occasions she'd asked him what his plans were, he'd simply brushed her off, telling her not to worry and that he was working on it. But how could she not worry? Time was running out.

Tired of Steven's feeble excuses, Tammy had lost her patience and was finding him intolerable. With only a week left before they had to vacate the apartment, she needed answers and she needed them now. Enough of this bullshit, she thought. She needed to know what he had planned for them. Even though she was fueled by a huge burden of anger and fear, she had to remind herself that Steven was the baby's father and now was not the time to abandon him. They were going to be a family and were in this together.

A few hours later, her questions were answered. Tammy was sneaking in a nap on the couch while Steven was at work, only to be jolted out of a deep sleep by the sound of someone barging through the front door. Startled and still exhausted, she sat up straight, her muscles tense with fear. "God, Steven, I was sleeping," she said as she patted her chest to calm her nerves, quickly realizing she wasn't in any danger. "You scared the hell out of me. Why all the noise?"

Throwing down his duffle bag by the door, he rushed over to the couch and dropped to his knees beside her. "Sorry, babe. Listen, I've got some great news." He beamed. "I've found us a place to live."

He grabbed her hand and squeezed it tight. "We can move in right away!"

Her eyes lost all signs of tiredness and sparkled with anticipation. Now he had her full attention. "Really? Where?"

Steven hesitated. "Seattle."

Flabbergasted, Tammy pushed Steven's hand away as a look of horror masked her face. "Seattle?" she screamed, unable to control her anger. "We can't move to bloody Seattle. Are you out of your fucking mind?" This was by far the stupidest thing she'd ever heard.

Steven grabbed her shoulders in an attempt to hold her interest. "Hear me out, okay. We can make this work. Look at it like a fresh start."

Tammy wasn't going to listen to him. She had no intentions of moving hundreds of miles away to another state. Pushing him away with the palms of her hands, she leapt up from the couch. "I'm not moving to Seattle, Steven. What about our jobs? And my dad? I can't just pack up and leave. It's just ridiculous. You can't be serious, surely?"

But he was serious. She could see it in his eyes. "It's the best I can do. We have no other choice." He stood and inched his way toward her. Still in shock, Tammy stumbled and allowed herself to fall freely into the chair next to her. Again, Steven knelt in front of her and took her hands. "It'll be okay. We can do this."

"Oh, I don't know, Steven. I'm sick of fucking up my life. Since I've been in this country, it's been one thing after another. I came here with the intentions of looking for Donna, but I've not done a fucking thing about it because crap keeps happening in my own stupid life. And now you want me to run away to Seattle? Yet another bloody hurdle."

"Your dad will call you if he hears anything about her. You know that. There's not much you can do because there's nothing to go on. We've talked about it before."

"I know, I know. But moving away from my dad feels like I'm abandoning her in some way. Not only that, like I've already said, we can't just quit our jobs. What are we supposed to live off for Christ's sake?"

A smug smile stretched across Steven's face. "Well, you didn't let me finish earlier, but I have a job waiting for me in Seattle."

Tammy was astonished. "You have a job?"

"Yep, I sure do. I can start as soon as we're settled."

"What kind of job? Is it with a restaurant?"

He hesitated again. "Actually, no. It's in sales."

Tammy creased her brow. "Sales? You've never sold a goddamn thing in your life. What will you be selling?"

Annoyed by her endless questioning, Steven gave her an answer that he hoped would satisfy her inquiring mind. "I don't know. I'll find out when we get there. They said I have the job, so I took it. We have a place to live and I have a job. What more do you want?"

"But, Steven, it's in bloody Seattle! How are we going to move all our stuff? My car's not big enough and we don't have the money to rent a moving van."

Steven rolled his eyes. "Its just stuff, Tammy. Our new place is fully furnished so we only need to take our clothes. We can just leave the rest here."

Tammy dragged her hands through her disheveled hair. "God, Steven I don't know. This just seems so bloody crazy." She couldn't believe she was even considering the idea. The thought of moving so far away with just a bag of clothes terrified the hell out of her.

Steven leaned in until his forehead was touching hers. Not wanting to cave in to his ludicrous idea, Tammy lowered her gaze to the floor.

Steven gave her a friendly shake. "Come on, Tammy, it'll be an adventure. You've always said you wanted to see more of the States. Well, now's your chance."

"Yes, I do. But this is all so sudden and so fast. Can't we find anything else? Something around here?" she pleaded.

"There's nothing. I've looked. Like you said, we don't have much time. I know it's far away, but we'll be fine. I promise."

Saying nothing, Tammy continued to stare at the floor as her mind buzzed with all the consequences they would have to suffer if they went through with Steven's crazy idea. She knew the only alternative she had was to move back to her father's, but she refused to do that again; she had too much pride. Tammy took a deep breath and looked up, her face painted with angst. "Okay, let's do it. Let's move to Seattle."

Steven's mouth fell wide open. "Really? Are you sure?"

"Yes, I'm sure. The hardest part will be telling my dad. I'll have to go and see him in person. I can't just call him on the phone and tell him."

Steven nodded, not wanting to discourage her decision in any way. "Sure, whatever you want to do is fine with me." He would agree to anything she wanted. After all, it was his fault they had to move. "I love you. You know that, don't you?"

Tammy kissed him on the lips and cupped his face in her hands. "I love you too, baby."

Tammy had avoided calling her father for two days, knowing the inevitable conversation wouldn't be an easy task. On the third day, she finally plucked up the courage to call. She told him she had some exciting news and would come over that afternoon.

At her father's house, Tammy sat at the table, her nerves on edge while she watched Joanne pour coffee for everyone. "So, don't keep us in suspense. What's the good news?" Joanne asked before taking a seat across from John, thankful that Andrew was down for a nap.

"Well, Steven was offered a job in Seattle and we're moving there at the end of the week."

Saying nothing, John and Joanne shared a quick glance at each other.

"Isn't that great?" Tammy added to break the silence.

Her father leaned back in his chair and folded his arms over his chest. "You're moving to Seattle?" he asked.

Joanne had her suspicions. Something wasn't adding up. "Why the sudden decision to move, Tammy? You've never talked about moving before today. Has something happened?" Joanne's mind raced with a million questions. Was she running away from something? Was Steven making her move? Was he in some sort of trouble? She had unsettling feelings about him, but Tammy seemed happy with him so she'd had to trust her judgment. This sudden move had her worried.

Tammy sensed Joanne's anxieties and, once again, she found herself covering for Steven. "Actually, we'd talked about it before Steven was offered the job in Seattle. He discussed it with me and I told him to take it. It pays more than what he's making now. It comes with a furnished place and he'll be able to start right away. I know it's sudden, but honestly, we couldn't pass it up."

John listened to his daughter's announcement with narrowed eyes and a feeling of uncertainty stirring in his gut. This didn't sit comfortably with him. "Are you absolutely sure about this, Tammy? You're right, it does seem rather hasty to say the least."

"I'm sure, Dad. Please, don't worry. I know what I'm doing. I'll be fine, and when the baby's born, we'll come down for a visit." She smiled at her father in an attempt to reassure him.

John reluctantly nodded, unfolded his arms, and glanced at

Joanne, "Well, I guess there's nothing more to say than for us to wish you luck."

"I guess not," Joanne agreed, displaying a subtle smile.

Relieved that they hadn't objected, Tammy walked over to her father and embraced him before giving him a peck on the cheek. "Thanks, Dad. I'm going to miss you guys, but I promise to keep in touch and bring the baby down to see you as often as we can."

He held on to her arm. "We're going to miss you, too," he said, an essence of concern still lingering in his voice. He couldn't help but wonder if bringing Tammy to the States was a mistake, just like it was with Donna.

CHAPTER 32

*D*on't you feel guilty for leaving all our stuff behind for Bill to deal with?" Tammy asked Steven as they walked out of their apartment for the last time, carrying only a bag of clothes each. "Don't you think it's kinda rude? I do," she added.

Steven walked in front of her with a bulky duffel bag draped over his right shoulder. "Nah, not at all. Look at it like we're leaving him the furniture in lieu of what we owe him for rent," he said as he approached the car, opened the trunk and tossed his bag freely inside, not caring where it landed.

"Yeah, I suppose so, but I can't help feeling like a criminal. I feel like we're running away and being totally irresponsible." She dropped her bag next to his and closed the trunk before jumping in the car next to Steven. Clearly not wanting to wait around for a second longer than necessary, he was already sitting in the driver's seat and revving the engine. "I still think we should tell work we're quitting. I hate to just leave without saying anything."

Steven began to back out of the driveway, wishing Tammy would just shut up and stop worrying about all the minor details. Unbeknown to Tammy, he owed money to a few people at work. If he showed up and announced he was quitting, there was a chance they'd start asking for their money back in front of Tammy. He couldn't allow that to happen. "It's better this way. I don't want to explain to everyone why we're moving. It's none of their business. Let's just go pick up our checks and get outta here."

Tammy silently rolled her eyes and sighed in defeat. Already tired from the whole ordeal, the last thing she wanted was to start an argument. She had to keep reminding herself this was for the best. They were about to start a new life with a new baby. Soon, this will all be behind them.

Over the course of the next hour, they had picked up their checks and cashed them at the bank before sitting back in the car to discuss their upcoming journey. Seattle was about eight hundred miles away. With few stops along the way, they estimated they could be there in roughly twelve hours.

"I'll drive the first leg because I have to make a quick stop," Steven said.

"A stop where?" Tammy asked, puzzled. She knew they already had everything they needed for the trip.

"It's just a quick stop. It'll only take a minute. Jeez, Tammy. What's with all the damn questions today?"

"Sorry," Tammy snapped, angered by his outburst. "I just didn't realize we had more stops to make."

Driving out of Lonesridge, the reality of what Tammy was doing slowly began to sink in. It reminded her of the time she left England. Leaving behind the securities of having her dad close by and unsure of where her future was headed this time around, Tammy's mind taunted her with doubts. Had her father been right? Had she been too hasty with her decision to leave town and move eight hundred miles away? She knew it was too late to turn around now. She just hoped, once again, she was doing the right thing.

About ten miles out of town, Steven exited the highway and turned left onto a desolate narrow dirt road.

"Where are we going?" Tammy asked.

"This is the stop I have to make. It'll only take a minute. I promise."

Tammy saw nothing but empty meadows and scattered oak trees through the clouds of dust that surrounded the car. As they continued down the bumpy road, she heard the barking of an agitated dog in the distance, which seemed to become louder and clearer as they slowly approached a house on the horizon. Driving closer, she saw it was more of a run-down shack than a house. Who could possibly live out here? Tammy wondered.

What was left of the flaky white paint was now peeling away from the wood. All the windows, a few of which were broken, had faded worn sheets hanging in front of them from inside the house. The German Shepherd, which was tied to a long rusty chain, continued its frenzied barking as they pulled up to the front. "Why have a pet if you're going to chain it up all day? It doesn't seem fair," she said to Steven as they came to a stop.

"I dunno. It's not my dog. Wait here," Steven ordered. "I'll be right back."

"Who lives out here?"

"It's just a buddy of mine. I owe him some money," he replied, fumbling with the door handle.

"Money for what?" Tammy screeched. They barely had enough to get to Seattle, let alone give money away to his so-called buddies. Tammy couldn't understand why he suddenly seemed so worried about paying someone back when he never bothered to pay any rent to their landlord for three whole months. It didn't make any bloody sense.

Steven had hoped to leave the car without being drilled with a bunch of questions, but she wasn't going to let that happen. "When I was short one month, he loaned me a few bucks."

"How much is a few bucks? The money we have is supposed to be for our drive," she protested.

"Quit worrying. We'll have enough," Steven snapped. With his back now toward her, he stepped out of the car and let the door swing shut. Crouching down, he looked at her through the open window. "I'll be back in a minute."

"Fine. Whatever." Tammy folded her arms in disgust, leaned back in her seat and closed her eyes, refusing to look at him.

Half an hour later, Steven returned. Furious, Tammy yelled, "What the fuck took you so fucking long?" She didn't wait for him to answer. "You said you'd only be a few minutes," she hollered as he got back in the car.

With no apology, he gave Tammy that same cocky grin that she'd grown to hate, started the car, and slid it into reverse. "Relax, okay?" he said, giving her knee a gentle squeeze.

Still angry, Tammy quickly slapped it away. "Don't touch me!"

"Oh, come on, don't be like that. I said I was sorry. We got to talking, and I lost track of time. But I'm here now. We have no more stops to make so we can get on the open road. Come on, babe, let's not start the trip like this."

"Well, stop pissing me off then." Tammy began to calm down. "I'm sorry I got mad but jeez, Steven, half an hour is a little more than five minutes. Do you blame me?"

"Yeah, I get it. But now we're going to Seattle! Woo-hoo!" he said with a beaming smile while shaking her arm. Tammy couldn't help but join him with a smile of her own. "That's better." Steven gleamed at her while putting the car in gear and headed for the main road. "Seattle, here we come!" he bellowed out of the window as they sped down the dirt road, leaving a trail of dust behind them.

Fourteen hours later, at three o'clock in the morning, they finally reached the dim streets of Seattle. Both tired from their trip, they decided to seek a motel for the rest of the night so they could get a good night's sleep and freshen up before calling Steven's new boss in the morning.

As they drove through the blocks hoping to find a vacancy sigh, Tammy began to feel uneasy. Homeless people lined the streets on both sides, sleeping in makeshift tents or cardboard boxes. Some were still awake, chugging liquor out of brown paper bags, and she swore she saw a prostitute or two stepping into vehicles on street corners.

"Steven, I don't think we're in a good part of town."

"Don't worry, it's only for one night. We'll be fine," he said, trying to ease her discomfort while scouting the neighborhood through the window. "There has to be a motel around here someplace."

Wanting to get off the streets as soon as possible, Tammy joined him in the hunt. For twenty minutes, they drove aimlessly up and down the darkened streets, their eyes fixed on each of the passing buildings. Tammy breathed a sigh of relief when she finally spotted a green "Vacancy" sign blinking brightly over a shadowed building on her right. "There's one!" she squealed with excitement, sitting bolt upright in her seat.

Steven lowered his head and glared out of her window. "Where?"

"There." Tammy pointed Steven in the right direction. "It's called The Lagoon."

Steven followed her finger. "Oh, I see it now." He pulled into the driveway of the motel, bringing the car to a stop in front of the office. Tammy waited in the car with the engine running while Steven left to get a room.

A few minutes later, he returned with key in hand and put the car in drive.

"Okay, we're in room 118. The guy at the desk said it's in the middle of the row of rooms on the left."

Tammy joined in the search, reading each room number illuminated by the dim lights of the parking lot while Steven inched the car along.

"There it is," Tammy said, pointing in the direction of the room with her finger.

Steven saw the room and pulled into the parking space in front, bringing the car to a stop. After grabbing their bags from the trunk, they both headed to the room, looking forward to crashing on the bed and getting some well-needed rest.

Disappointment flooded Tammy as soon as she entered the dark and dingy motel room. Overpowered by the odor of damp, musty air, she covered her nose and mouth with her hands. "My god, this is bloody awful," Tammy muffled through the material of her sleeves. She glanced at the vile orange and gold wallpaper in horror and then down at the stains covering the bright orange shag carpet. Her eyes turned to the queen-size bed, topped with a thin, faded orange bed- spread. She shuddered at the thought of sleeping in it.

Steven tossed their bags on the bed and the keys on a small wooden table beneath the TV, which was padlocked to a metal rack high on the wall.

If the room itself was this bad, Tammy dreaded the thought of how the other facilities were going to look. Adjusting to the foul smell of the room, she removed her hands from her face and cautiously made her way over to the door she assumed lead to their bathroom. "Jesus Christ! This is disgusting!" she hollered to Steven as she quickly recovered her face. "How could anyone feel clean bathing in this filth?" She walked across the cracked white tiled floor to the single sink, blotched with rust and other questionable blemishes. "Ugh," she mumbled. To her right was a small shower, shielded with a clear plastic shower curtain. At least, it would've been clear if it weren't for the years of soap scum clinging to it. Tammy peaked behind the curtain. "Fucking gross," she grumbled, eying the paint peeling away from the filthy tiles and the blackened mold growing around the edges.

"Are you done?" Steven called from the room. "I need to use the bathroom."

Tammy reappeared. "I don't know that you should go in there... you might never come out alive," she said, laughing, and then she turned serious. "You know, you don't have to go in the bathroom to take your medicine, Steven. I'm okay with it."

"Huh?" Steven looked puzzled, and then he remembered the diabetic thing. "Oh, yeah. No thanks, I prefer it this way."

She raised her hands in surrender. "Sorry, sorry. Just trying to make it easier for you. Go ahead. It's all yours," she said as she slithered pass him and perched on the edge of the bed. "I'm glad we're only here for one night. This place is bloody awful."

"It's not that bad," Steven said with a grin before closing the bathroom door behind him.

Contemplating if she should take off her shoes or not, she quickly opted for the latter when she spotted a cockroach scurrying across the carpet. "Yuck!" she squealed, flinging her feet up on the bed. With the decision made not to remove her shoes or clothes, Tammy lay down on top of the bedspread and cringed as her head sank into the musty pillow. Despite her ill feelings toward the horrendous accommodation, exhaustion soon took over and Tammy drifted off to sleep.

Fifteen minutes later, Steven crept out of the bathroom. The subtle sound of Tammy's light snoring was music to his ears. Letting out a sigh of relief, he uttered, "Finally, she's asleep." Knowing he would need his rig first thing in the morning, he'd taped it above the water line inside the toilet tank; a hiding place he had often used at home since Tammy found his previous spot under the sink.

As the effects of the drug rushed through his veins, an amazing feeling of warmth and calmness smothered his entire body. The drug was telling him that life was good. Staring at the bed, his eyes and head began to feel heavy. He let his body fall like a lifeless rag doll onto the bedspread, not caring where or how he landed, and drifted off into a deep, drug-induced sleep shortly after.

CHAPTER 33

he next morning, Tammy was rudely awakened by the
sound of screaming voices coming from the parking
lot outside. She raised her arm and squinted at her watch,
angered to see that it was only five o'clock. Looking over at
Steven, she envied him, blatantly undisturbed by the commotion
outside.

"You're a fucking pig!" Tammy heard a female voice scream in a
drunken slur.

"Oh, go fuck yourself," a drunken male voice replied.

For the next hour, Tammy lay motionless in the dark. She
chose not to turn on the lights or peek through the curtains in fear
of being seen.

Frustrated and fatigued, Tammy had had enough and jabbed
Steven on the arm with her elbow. "Steven, wake up." She jabbed
him again but with more force. "Steven! Wake up! I want to get out
of here." After a few more attempts, he finally began to stir.

In a drowsy state, he strained to open his eyes. "What's wrong?"
he mumbled.

"Don't you hear that racket outside? It's been going on for over an hour. Let's get out of this dump. This place sucks," she said, jumping up from the bed and grabbing her bag.

Steven pulled his body up to a sitting position and rubbed his eyes, realizing he wouldn't be allowed to go back to sleep. "Don't you want to shower first and freshen up?"

"I'm not stepping foot in that bathroom, it's horrible. Cockroaches are crawling all over the place. I can't stand it here. Come on. Get up," she ordered as she stood impatiently by the door.

Needing a fix, Steven rose from the bed and tried to smooth out his wrinkled clothes with his hands before walking to the bathroom.

"Where are you going?" Tammy asked. "To the bathroom. I'll just be a minute and then we'll go, okay?"

"God, Steven. You're always in the bloody bathroom! Hurry up will you. I hate this place," she barked as she stormed across the room and took a seat at the table, folding her arms in protest.

Not wanting to piss her off even more, he rushed into the bathroom, quickly closed the door behind him, and double checked it was locked securely. The last thing he needed was her deciding he was taking too long and charging through the door in the middle of a fix. He hurried through his usual morning ritual, retrieved the rig, and hid it in the back pocket of his jeans. In record time, he had completed his task and joined Tammy in the room where he found her still brooding at the table.

Welcoming the sudden rush, Tammy's bitter mood didn't faze him—nothing did when he was high. "Okay, I'm ready. Wanna grab breakfast someplace? It's too early to call my boss."

"Sure, but not in this bloody neighborhood."

Steven slung his bag over his shoulder and opened the door. "Will you cheer up? We're leaving. Get your stuff and let's go."

Tammy dragged her bags off the table and followed Steven out the door.

For the next fifteen minutes, Steven hunted for a restaurant that would please Tammy and hopefully bring her out of her foul mood. Having already turned down numerous places due to them looking "dirty," she finally agreed to a Denny's, so Steven spun into the parking lot at full speed before she could change her mind.

Still giving Steven the silent treatment, Tammy tucked her purse under her arm and exited the car, slamming the door behind her.

"Jeez, Tammy, what's your problem? Easy on the car door, will you," Steven yelled, using his response as a distraction while he discreetly placed his rig underneath the driver's seat. Ignoring him, Tammy continued to march toward the entrance. Steven quickened his pace to catch up with her and finally reached her as she was opening the restaurant door.

While they sat and waited for a table, Steven tried to sooth Tammy's mood by taking her hand. "Are you okay?"

She jolted her hand away. "That motel was just horrible. I can't believe you let us stay there."

Steven retrieved her hand, stroking it gently with his fingers. This time, she didn't pull away. "Relax, babe, okay? It's behind us. We were both exhausted and took the first place we saw."

"I know. It just gave me the creeps. I've never stayed in such a filthy place before."

"Me neither," Steven lied.

"It's okay," Tammy said, sighing. "It's behind me. I'm sorry."

"I'm sorry, too," Steven replied, finishing with a make up kiss on her lips. Once seated and in better spirits, they feasted on a hearty breakfast of pancakes, eggs, and sausage.

"Hey, babe, I need to go make a phone call to see where we need to go," Steven said to Tammy after finishing their meal.

"Okay. I'll wait here. In fact, after you get back, I should call my dad and Joanne and let them know we made it to Seattle. It was too late to call from the motel last night. They'll be worried sick if I don't."

"Good idea. I'll be right back." Confident she wouldn't leave the table, Steven left to find a phone booth.

"Hey, Rick, it's Steven. How's it going, man?"

"Hey, man. You guys here yet?"

"Yeah. We're somewhere in downtown Seattle."

"Oh, you're not too far away then. I'd guess about seventeen miles. You just need to head north on Highway 99 and take the exit for 212th Street." Rick continued to give directions while Steven made notes on a scrap of paper he had found in his pocket.

"Great, thanks, man. We should be there shortly. And, Rick, one more thing." Steven turned his head, confirming Tammy was still at the booth.

"Yeah, what's that, man?"

"Tammy doesn't know what I'm selling. I just told her it's a sales job."

"I understand, man. I gotcha back."

"Thanks, bro, we'll see you soon," Steven said before hanging up the phone and returning to the table. Steven slid into the booth and took a sip of the now cold coffee.

"Hey, babe, we're not too far from where we need to go. It's about another seventeen miles. We should be there in about half an hour."

"Great!" Tammy slid out from the booth. "I'm going to call my dad and Joanne. Can you get me a refill on the coffee? I won't be long." she said before leaving to make her call.

After a ten-minute call with Joanne describing their long drive, leaving out the horrible motel details, Tammy returned to the table and took a seat.

"I wonder what our new place is like. I hope it's nothing like that motel."

Steven had no idea, only that Rick had told him they could stay with him. "I'm sure it won't be. It's in a town called Knottsby. Apparently, it's a small waterfront town."

"Oh, wow, I can't wait to see it. I've never lived by the water. Isn't that where all the rich people live? Come on, let's go," she said as she jumped from the booth. "I'll meet you at the car."

"No, wait...um, I don't have enough money to pay for this," Steven confessed.

Tammy turned and glared at Steven. "What do you mean, you don't have enough money?" she asked in a loud, angry whisper. "You just got paid, for Christ's sake!" She quickly scanned the restaurant to make sure no one overheard.

Steven followed her whisper. "Yes, and it's gone. I owed that guy money, remember? Then there was gas and the motel room..."

"You only paid for gas once, I paid for the rest. How much did you give that guy? Oh, do you know what, never mind. I don't want to know. Just give me the bloody check," Tammy snarled as she snatched it from his hand. "I'll meet you outside." She stormed off to pay the check, shaking her head in disgust.

With tension between them once again, Tammy sat in silence for the most part of the journey. She was trying to calculate in her head where Steven's money had gone—it wasn't adding up. "So, how much did you give that guy? I can't believe you've spent *all* your money."

Refusing to look at her, Steven tilted his head back and rolled his eyes; he didn't want to have this conversation. "I don't remember. It doesn't matter anyway."

"You don't remember?" she asked, puzzled. "It was just yesterday! How can you not remember? And yes, it does matter, Steven. We have no more money coming in until you get paid from your new job, and who knows when that will be."

Tired of her nitpicking and unable to explain that he'd had to buy some tar to make the trip to Seattle without going through withdrawals, Steven tried to reason with her. "I'll be making some money tomorrow. Will you stop worrying? We'll be fine," he said, hoping she would just drop it and shut up.

But she wouldn't. "I just can't believe you spent it all. You had more than I did, and I still have half of my check left."

Again, Steven rolled his eyes. Losing his patience, he tightened his grip on the steering wheel and let his temper flare. "God, Tammy, will you fucking shut up! I told you, I'll be working tomorrow and I'll have some money. Now can we please just drop it?"

Surprise by his rage—never had he expressed such venom toward her—she stared at his dark, hollow eyes and watched his body tremble with anger. She feared he might strike out at her if she said anything more, so she retreated her voice to a much calmer state. "Fine," she mumbled. Tammy folded her arms and stewed in her seat without saying another word for the rest of the journey.

Twenty minutes later, they pulled into the driveway of a modest single-story home and parked behind a black Chevy van. Tammy opened her door and stepped out, welcoming the fresh, cool breeze, especially after sitting in a stale car with no air conditioning for the best part of the last twenty-four hours. Scanning the street, she liked what she saw. It seemed like a quiet neighborhood, with modest, single-family homes in decent condition on either side of the road.

With their long journey finally coming to an end, the argument between them was soon forgotten. Elated to have arrived, Steven walked around the car with a joyful skip in his gait to join Tammy. He grabbed her hand and pulled her toward the front door. "Come on, let's go find Rick."

She followed close behind Steven as he led the way to the front door and knocked. When the door opened, they were greeted by a heavy-set guy, wearing Levis and a white t-shirt. His long black hair was tied loosely in a ponytail and reached the middle of his back.

"Steven, my man! You made it," Rick cheered, pulling Steven into a hug and slapping his back with a meaty hand.

Rick was not how Tammy had imagined. She had pictured him thinner with short hair, clean-shaven, and having a more professional wardrobe—maybe a suit and tie. After all, he was in sales;

his rather rough-looking attire didn't seem appropriate for his line of work.

"Rick, dude! It's been a long time, man."

Rick glanced over Steven's shoulder in the direction of Tammy. "And this must be the beautiful Tammy I've heard so much about?" he said with a smile aimed at her.

Tammy smiled back and nodded, shuffling her feet towards Steven.

"Yeah, this is my Tammy," Steven said proudly, wrapping his arm around her shoulder and pulling her in closer.

"Nice to meet you, Tammy."

"You too, Rick," Tammy replied.

"Well, come on in, guys," Rick said, gesturing them inside with a sweep of his muscular arm. He led them through a dark hallway to a small kitchen at the back of the house, which looked slightly bigger than it was due to the white painted cupboards and the two windows looking out onto the back yard. He pulled out two chairs from the table in the middle of the room.

"Here, have a seat. Can I get you guys a beer?" Rick asked while opening the door to the fridge.

"Sure, I'll take one," Steven replied. "No, thanks...I'm pregnant. Do you have any juice?"

Rick looked up from behind the fridge door. "You're pregnant? Steven, why didn't you tell me?"

Steven flashed a playful wink at Tammy. "I dunno. Figured I'd surprise you."

"You certainly did that. Wow!" Rick said, rooting through the fridge again. "I only have apple juice. Will that do?"

"Yes, that's fine."

Rick placed a bottle in front of her on the table. "Here ya go."

"Thank you."

Rick popped the caps off the bottles of Budweiser and joined them at the table. "I love your accent. British, right?"

Tammy finished her sip of apple juice. "Yes, that's right. I can't seem to hide it," she said, chuckling.

"Oh, don't ever do that," Rick replied.

"I won't," she said. "I like your home by the way."

"Oh, it's not mine. It's my parents'. They're in Alaska for three months. So, right now, I have the place all to myself," Rick said, nudging Steven's elbow.

Tammy guessed he was probably in his mid-thirties and found it odd that he still lived with his parents, but she tried not to act too surprised. "Oh, I see."

"Yeah, works out great. It means you can stay here until they get back. That should give you enough time to find a place."

"Yeah, that's cool, man. Thanks," Steven said.

"Can I see where we'll be staying?" Tammy asked.

"Sure, it's out back." Rick scooted his chair away from the table, grabbed his beer, and headed toward the back door. "Follow me."

Tammy wrinkled her forehead. "Out back?" she whispered to Steven.

Steven shrugged his shoulders and proceeded to follow Rick.

Tammy followed in silence. They stepped out onto a large wooden deck while Rick held the door open. Off to one side was a round plastic patio table and four chairs, all of which looked like they might have once been white. Tammy glanced over at the dozens of empty beer bottles scattered on the table and shuddered at the sight of at least half a dozen tuna fish cans full of cigarette butts. They followed Rick down the wooden steps from the patio and walked across the grass to the far corner of the yard. A silver-colored travel trailer came in to view behind the broken remains of an old storage shed. Rick opened the door to the trailer and stepped inside.

"It's not much, and it needs a bit of a cleaning I'm afraid, but I'm sure it'll work for a few months."

Horrified by what Rick was proposing, Tammy froze outside the doorway and gasped. "You can't be serious? It's a bloody caravan!"

"It's a what?" Rick asked, sticking his head back out the door.

"A caravan. People go on holidays in these things. They don't *live* in them!" Tammy squealed, still stunned.

Steven reached for her hand. "Over here, babe, we call them travel trailers."

Tammy quickly pushed his hand away in a temper. "I've never heard of living in a bloody caravan. There's not enough friggin' room for starters."

Rick yelled from inside. "It's not that bad, Tammy. Come on in and take a look."

Reluctantly, Tammy climbed the skinny metal steps and entered. She saw straight away that it was even smaller than she had imagined. Gulping down her anger, she began to walk through what was to be her new home. A strong musty smell lingered in the air, making her cough, but she soon realized her sudden bad chest might have been caused by the thick layer of dust coating every surface. The pasty yellow color of the cabinets and couch made her feel like she was stepping back into the sixties. The kitchen was the tiniest she had ever seen, with only enough standing room for one person, but it did have the necessities: a single sink, a small white fridge, and a built-in cooker with a small oven.

Walking to the end of the trailer, she passed a small bathroom, consisting of a yellow toilet, a tiny yellow shower, which she had no idea how she was going to fit into once her bump got bigger, and a miniature stainless sink tucked in the corner.

She reached the back of the trailer in no more than an extra three strides and found herself standing in the bedroom. With the bare mattress taking up most of the floor space, she stood still and glanced around the rest of the poky room. Overhead cabinets hung from the back wall with two brass sconce lights on either side. In earlier days, the drapes throughout the living space probably had a yellow floral print that looked quite pretty. But now, they were torn, rotten, and faded from years of being exposed to the sunlight. The carpet wasn't any better, fraying in most places and blotched with a patchwork of stains.

Rick took a sip of his beer and turned to Tammy, who was now standing in the area of the trailer known as the kitchen—she couldn't see herself ever calling it a kitchen. "See, it's not too bad," he said.

Steven was waiting by the door to the trailer, opting to keep quiet and trying to avoid the solemn look on Tammy's face.

Tammy leaned against the sink and folded her arms. "Does the plumbing work? Is there even running water?"

"I'm afraid not. It's not hooked up. But the back door to the house is always open, so you can shower and use the bathroom over there," Rick said cheerfully before chugging down more beer. "The stove doesn't work either, but you can cook in the kitchen of the house if you want."

"I guess we don't have a choice." Tammy scowled and turned to Steven. "Do we, Steven?"

"Come on, Tammy. At least it's a roof over our heads."

"Oh, hush Steven. If I'd known you expected me to live in a bloody caravan, I would never have come here in the first place."

Thinking they needed some privacy, Rick butted in. "I'll leave you two alone," he said before quickly exiting the trailer.

Tammy nodded and continued where she left off. "I'm not raising our child in a goddamn caravan, Steven. I'll tell you that right now."

"We won't be. It's just temporary," Steven said in a reassuring voice.

"You're damn right it's temporary!" Tammy shouted. "Even if it means I have to look for a place on my own...a place with running water, I might add." Holding her nose and coughing, Tammy headed to the door. "I have to get out of here, it stinks."

Steven was left behind to wonder how on earth he was going to fix his latest mess.

CHAPTER 34

ammy spent the next three days scrubbing the trailer from top to bottom, lugging buckets of warm, soapy water from the main house. Rick had given her a pile of sheets and pillowcases, some of which she used for the windows after pulling down the old curtains.

By the third day, she had managed to wash all the walls and clean all the cupboards inside and out. The place was at least livable now, if not somewhat cozy. The only area left to clean was the bathroom. After emptying everything from the cupboard below the vanity, she spent a few hours washing the walls, the shower stall, and the small sink. She then bagged up all the items from the vanity, which included an old hairbrush, a rusty can of shaving cream, old razors, and a plastic storage bag. Before tossing the bag, she opened it and peered inside. Sticky black tar with a strong odor of vinegar caused her to hold her breath. "Ugh, disgusting!" she said, whipping her head in the opposite direction.

Feeling satisfied with the much cleaner state of the bathroom, Tammy grabbed the large black trash bag and headed out to the driveway. Pleased to see the trash truck was at the house next door, she waited by the curb and waved to the guy standing on the back of the truck.

As it pulled up in front of her and came to a stop, Tammy held up the bag and yelled, "Can you take this one please?"

The man jumped off the truck and approached her. "Sure, darling," he said with a cheeky grin and a wink.

Ignoring his flirtatious manner, Tammy handed him the bag. "Thank you," she said before heading back up the driveway.

Happy with her progress on the trailer and not expecting Steven to return until after dark, she decided to treat herself to a shower and some lunch.

Since arriving at Rick's, Steven had changed dramatically. Rarely did they see or even talk to each other. Using her car, they left early in the morning before she was awake, and Steven would always leave a twenty-dollar bill on the small dinette table. She used the money to buy cleaning supplies and lunch for herself from the small market at the end of their street.

Always returning home after dark, usually in a delirious state, Steven never said more than few words to Tammy. She watched from afar as he flopped onto the couch with his eyelids drooping halfway over his reddened eyes. He invariably nodded off on the couch with his head bent forward in a drowsy state as Tammy looked on in disgust. Sometimes, straining to stay awake, he'd jerk up in a moment of panic, but within a few seconds, he'd nod off again, incoherent and oblivious to Tammy's presence. Appalled by his appearance and erratic behavior, Tammy often slept in the bed alone. By the time she woke up, he was gone again.

On her way to take a shower the following morning, Tammy couldn't avoid the dirty dishes piled high in the sink of the main house and decided to wash them. Above the clatter of dishes and cutlery, she thought she heard a noise coming from the back yard. Slowly raising her hands out of the soapy water and giving them a brisk shake, she stood in silence and listened intently for any more sounds outside. A few seconds went by before she heard the roaring holler of a male voice and what sounded like objects crashing against a wall.

Puzzled, Tammy ran to the back door and out into the yard. "What the hell is going on?" she grumbled. Turning her head from side-to-side, she scanned the entire area and tried to tune in on where the commotion was coming from. Another round of shouting confirmed the noise was coming from the trailer.

From inside, she heard Steven yell, "Where the fuck is it?"

Alarmed, Tammy ran as fast as she could to the entranceway and nervously peeked her head through the door. Horrified by what she saw, she slapped her hands over her open mouth and gasped in shock. The trailer she had just spent three days diligently cleaning and trying to make a home out of, had seemingly been destroyed in a matter of minutes. Every drawer had been pulled out and their broken contents were now scattered across the floor in a state of disarray. The once neatly organized stacks of plates and cups now lay in ruins beneath her feet, and the few cupboard doors that hadn't been torn from their hinges were open and swinging freely.

Steven, still unaware of Tammy's presence, was now in the bedroom with his back facing her. As Tammy raced in his direction, fueled with hatred, she could see the bed had been torn apart. Sheets and blankets were tossed into corners, and the mattress lay on its side against a wall. In a blind rage, Steven was pulling everything out of the cupboards above the bed and launching their belongings around the room.

Diving between the flying objects, Tammy ran over to him. "Steven! Stop! What are you doing?" she yelled while grabbing him by the shoulders and pulling him back.

He spun around with a fiery glint in his eyes and locked his fingers around her arms. "Where is it, Tammy? What did you do with the bag?" Steven screamed as he rattled her body back and forth under his tight grip.

Bracing against the pain of his fingernails digging into her flesh, Tammy cried out, "Steven, you're hurting me!" Terrified, she looked into his eyes, shadowed by a haunting darkness of a man she no longer knew.

"WHERE'S THE FUCKING BAG, TAMMY?"

"What bag? I don't know what you're talking about," Tammy sobbed.

"The bag that was underneath the sink in the bathroom. I know I left it there but now it's gone." Steven shook her harder. "What did you do with it? ANSWER ME!" he screamed in Tammy's face so loud that spots of spittle flew out of his mouth and landed on her pale skin.

"Steven, you're scaring me." She was choking on her words, trembling with fear. "There was nothing under there but trash."

Unable to see through the veil of unshed tears, she sniffed hard to clear her nose. "The only bag under there was a plastic bag with some old brown stuff in it."

Steven froze. His eyes shot wide open with hope. "That's the one! What did you do with it?"

"I...um...I th-threw it away. I thought, um...I thought it was rubbish."

As a wave of panic flushed through him, he released his grip on Tammy and spun around before storming back through the trailer, scanning the wreckage for any kind of trash bag. "Where's the trash bag you put it in?" Digging through piles of clutter, he yelled louder, "Where is it, Tammy?"

"I gave it to the trash man. He pulled up right when I was walking out to the driveway."

"You did...fuck...you did what?" As a look of horror descended over Steven's face, he raised his right hand high above his shoulder and swung it down across the left side of her face.

From the unexpected force of his strike, Tammy collapsed against the wall and slid down to the floor. Cupping her cheek in her hand, she felt a hot throbbing pain beneath her skin. Petrified by his enraged state and unable to understand what had come over him, she cowered beneath the shelter of her shaking hands. "I'm sorry, I didn't know," she whispered, her voice trembling with fear.

Steven's shadow loomed over her, his eyes blazing and his nostrils flaring with anger. He mocked her by impersonating a female voice. "I didn't know..." Before Tammy realized what he was doing, his left foot barreled hard into her stomach.

Squealing in pain, she curled up into a fetal position and held her stomach tight. "My god, Steven! The baby!" she screamed as a cascade of tears poured down her face.

Ignoring Tammy's anguish, Steven jabbed her sharply on the shoulder and snarled, "That was five thousand dollars' worth of stuff. I was going to use it to get us outta here. Now what are we going to do?"

Tammy had no idea what he was talking about, nor did she care. Her only worry now was about the baby, unlike Steven, who showed no concern whatsoever. Through her sobbing, she heard someone enter the trailer and the thud of heavy footsteps making their way toward them. In silence, Tammy gushed with relief.

"Hey, Steven, you in here?" she heard Rick call.

Steven held a finger up to his lips, instructing Tammy to be quiet. "Not now, man."

She ignored his request. "In here, Rick!" she hollered back.

Rick appeared in the doorway just in time to see Steven punishing Tammy for not keeping her mouth shut by slapping her across the back of her head. Horrified by what he witnessed, Rick rushed over to Steven, grabbed his arms, and yanked him away from Tammy. "Whoa, man. What the fuck's going on?"

"The stupid bitch threw away the bag, man," Steven moaned, struggling to break loose from Rick's firm hold. Ignoring Steven's protests, Rick turned to Tammy, who was still sobbing on the floor. "Are you okay?"

Afraid to speak again, Tammy simply nodded.

"I'll be right back," Rick said as he began to walk Steven out of the room. "Come on, man, let's get you some fresh air. You need to calm down."

Outside the trailer, with enough distance between them and Tammy, Rick let Steven go.

"I'm so fucked, man!" Steven griped while fumbling for a cigarette in his jean pocket.

"Don't sweat about the stuff right now. Jeez." Rick took a cigarette from Steven, lit it, and inhaled deeply. "Why'd you hit her? She doesn't know what's going on. Damn, man." He drew a few more deep hits off the cigarette and stomped it out on the ground. "Stay here while I go talk to your girl."

Rick found Tammy still curled in the fetal position on the floor, sobbing and holding her stomach. Kneeling beside her, Rick took her in his arms. "Shh, it's going to be okay."

Tammy welcomed his embrace and huddled her head against his chest. Rick held her tight, letting her cry until she was ready to speak.

"I don't know what I did wrong, Rick. There was nothing but trash under the sink." She pulled herself away from his arms and leaned against the wall before stretching out her legs and placing her hands back over her stomach. "I've never seen him so angry. No one has ever hit me before, not even my father. I'm worried about the baby, Rick. He kicked me in my stomach."

"I'm sure the baby's fine. Do you have any cramps or pain?"

Tammy shook her head.

"And you're not bleeding. Right?"

Again, she shook her head.

Rick knew he had to come clean with her; she had a right to know. He placed a hand on her knee. "Tammy, the stuff in the plastic bag that you threw away was five thousand dollars' worth of heroin."

"It was what?" she asked, puzzled.

"Heroin," he repeated. "It's a narcotic drug...and, um, Steven is selling it for me. He should've told you all this before dragging you up here. We go way back. We've known each other since high school and used to get high together."

Tammy stared at Rick in shock. She couldn't believe what he was telling her. "Steven uses drugs?"

"I thought you knew." He was stunned that she didn't. "Haven't you noticed the tracks, or I guess you can call them scars, on his arms? Haven't you found any needles?"

"I did find needles once in our old apartment back in Lonesridge." Suddenly, it hit her. Steven had been lying to her from the beginning. "I confronted him, but because I didn't really know what they were for, I asked why he never told me he was a diabetic."

Rick chuckled. "Sorry, I don't mean to laugh. You really thought he was a diabetic? And I guess Steven played along, hmm?"

Tammy nodded, but she still wasn't totally convinced. "But diabetics do use needles, and he has the scars to prove it."

"Honey, insulin shots don't leave scars. Those scars are from using heroin. I hate to tell you this, but Steven's been shooting up heroin for as long as I've known him."

"Shooting up? What does that mean?" Tammy asked.

"I'm sorry. It's a term used for getting high with needles."

Tammy frowned. "You mean like...injecting drugs to get high?"

Rick nodded.

"Do you shoot up?" she asked.

"I stopped about four years ago. Now I just sell the stuff."

"And you offered Steven a job?"

"Steven contacted me a while back. Said he needed to get out of town and asked if I was still selling. When I said yes, he said he wanted in. He said he was bringing his girl with him. I assumed you knew everything, so I told him I'd set him up and that the both of you could stay here for a while."

"He hadn't paid our rent in over three months. That's why we got kicked out. He told me he had a job in sales."

"Well, he wasn't lying about that. He just didn't tell you what he was selling."

"I can't believe I never knew he was a drug user." Tammy thought for a moment. "What if I tell him I don't want him to use or sell drugs anymore. Do you think he'll quit?"

Feeling sorry for her, Rick shook his head. She was so naive and clearly had no idea what she was up against. "Tammy, he's an addict...a junkie. Some people are addicted to alcohol. Steven is addicted to heroin, but the addiction to heroin is a hundred times worse than being addicted to booze. Heroin is one of the most powerful and addictive drugs out there. He's not going to be able to just quit. It's not that easy. He'd risk suffering from life-threatening withdrawals."

Tammy knelt on her knees and faced Rick. "But you quit, so why can't he?"

"I spent over three years going in and out of rehab before I became clean. I couldn't have done it alone. I needed help. With medication and counseling, I gradually weaned myself off the drug, and I can tell you now that it was one of the hardest things I've ever had to do. It's dangerous of me to still sell the drug, and yeah, I'm not gonna lie, the temptation is still there, but every day I get a little bit stronger. Now it's all about the money. I make damn good money selling the stuff. More than I could ever make doing a normal job."

Tammy pulled herself to her feet and began pacing the room, combing her hair with her fingers, deep in thought. "Well, what am I going to do? I don't want my baby around drugs, or living in this trailer for that matter. Surely, the baby will make him want to quit."

Rick rose to his feet and walked over to her, placing his hand on her shoulder. Tammy met his gaze. "Look, Tammy, I can't tell you what to do. You need to make your own decisions. But you're right, a kid shouldn't be raised in this kind of lifestyle. I hope he can quit for the sake of the baby, and for your sake, too. But, the sad part is, neither one of us can make him quit. He has to do it on his own."

Trying to comfort herself, Tammy folded her arms. "And what about the stuff I threw away? I'm so sorry, Rick, I had no idea what it was. I honestly thought it was trash."

"Don't worry about it. I'll work it out with Steven." He didn't want to tell her that Steven would have to give him a higher cut on future batches to cover the lost until the five thousand was paid back. Right now, he was just thankful he had some extra cash stashed away to pay the dealer for the batch she had thrown away. "Well, it looks like you have a lot of thinking to do. I'm going to leave you alone. Are you going to be okay?"

"Yeah I'll be fine, and thank you."

Still feeling sorry for her but knowing there was nothing more he could do, Rick left the trailer to go find Steven. After a quick lap of the yard and the house, Rick realized he was nowhere to be found.

Left alone in her thoughts, Tammy questioned why she hadn't seen the signs of Steven's drug use. Reflecting back, they all seemed so clear now; his constant mood swings, falling asleep in the middle of the day—sometimes in front of company—the needles under the sink, his frequent long visits to the bathroom and how he seemed much happier when he came out wearing that awful smirk she detested, the fact that he never paid rent yet still had no money. She also realized now that the stop they'd made to see his "buddy" outside of Lonesridge was a place he needed to stop at to buy drugs—no wonder he wanted her to stay in the car.

Maybe she didn't want to know. Maybe she was in denial. Perhaps the hardest part to accept was that her father had known the whole time. He'd even tried to tell her, warn her, but she'd refused to listen. Steven had been lying to her for months. She was having a baby with someone she didn't even know. Today, she had seen the monster within. No matter what she did, she couldn't get through to him. His one and only concern was the drugs; not her, not the baby.

Tammy found herself fearing him, afraid of what he may be capable of when under the spell of the drug. She could no longer trust him and would have to tread carefully to ensure she didn't cause him to explode. She needed time to think. Was she willing to give him another chance? She didn't know right now. Her priority was to find her and the baby a better home and a better life.

She had to take the reins to get her life back. She had to stand up for herself and not allow herself to cower under him. Tomorrow would be a new start. She would begin by taking her car back so Steven could no longer use it for drug deals. She would spend the day looking for a job and wouldn't return until her hunt proved successful.

CHAPTER 35

*E*ven though Tammy was still sore from being kicked in the stomach, she somehow managed to clean the whole trailer again following Steven's rampage. She put items back in the cupboards and threw away anything that was broken or destroyed. She struggled with the mattress on her own and pulled it back on the box spring before remaking the bed, hanging all the clothes back in the closets, and putting the cushions back on the sofa. Rick popped in from time to time to check on her, making sure she was okay and to see if Steven had returned, but he had not.

By nine o'clock, Tammy was exhausted, both physically and emotionally. Her body ached from head to toe and her stomach was still sore to touch. Periodically, she rubbed it gently to sooth the pain. Relieved she hadn't bled or bruised, she was certain the baby was okay.

Shortly after settling on the couch with her feet up, a pillow behind her head, and a magazine in her hands, she saw the reflection of bright headlights from a car pulling into the driveway. She listened as the engine came to a stop. A few seconds later, she heard the creek of the car door open and then a thud as it was closed. With attentive ears, she listened to the sound of heavy foot-steps, growing louder as they approached the trailer. Knowing it was Steven, she wondered if he was still angry and felt a rush of adrenaline as her body switched into fight or flight mode. Should she have fled before he came home? No, she couldn't. She had nowhere to go and besides, he had her car.

Hearing the thud of his boots on the metal steps, Tammy froze. Holding her breath, she watched the handle of the door move down as Steven pulled it open from the other side. Her heart pounded with dread as she waited for him to enter. When he appeared in the doorway, her heart instantly melted. She felt crushed. Never had she seen a man look so sad. His swollen red eyes told her he'd been crying. His hair was in disarray, his pants were dirty, and damp stains blotted his white t-shirt from his tears.

He took one look at Tammy and fell to his knees next to the couch, sobbing loudly. "I'm so sorry, Tammy," he cried. "I don't know what came over me. Please forgive me."

With tears of her own, Tammy reached out and cupped his head in her palms. Softly stroking his hair as he nestled his head on her stomach, she felt pity toward him. He was crouched before her like a little lost boy. "Shh, it's okay. I know," she said, holding him tight.

With tears rolling down his cheeks, Steven pulled himself up to meet her eyes. "I love you, Tammy. I never meant to hurt you. It will never happen again, I promise."

With her eyes scrunched closed, Tammy kissed him long and hard on the top of his head before burying her face in his hair. She saw the remorse in his eyes. She had to believe him. They still had a chance to be a family. She wasn't going to give up so easy. "I forgive you," she whispered. Releasing her hold on him and pulling herself together, Tammy sat up and patted the cushion next to her. "Come on, get off the floor and sit next to me. We need to talk."

Sniffing back a tear, his head hung low, he silently obeyed her.

Tammy took his hand. "I love you too, Steven, but you scared me today...more than I've ever been scared in my whole life. All this time you've been lying to me about the drugs and your new job in *sales*."

"I'm sorry I lied to you, but I didn't know how to tell you. I was afraid you'd leave me if you knew."

"I want to trust you, Steven." She took a deep breath. "I'm willing to start over and put all this behind us if you will too, but..." Letting go of his hand, Tammy sat up straight with a serious frown.

"But what?"

"In order for me to stay, there have to be some changes." She gazed into his sorry eyes, telling herself not to give in. "I won't raise our child in this trailer and I want there to be no more drugs. I don't want you selling them and I don't want you using them. Do I make myself clear?"

She had no idea what she was asking from him. Nevertheless, Steven gave a silent nod.

Tammy rose from the couch and began pacing the room. "I mean it, Steven. Tomorrow, I'm going to look for work. I'll be taking my car and I'm not coming home until I have a job. And you can do the same. Go out and get a real job. You can tell Rick in the morning that you're done. He knows I'm having a baby. I'm sure he'll understand."

Steven's agitation was niggling at him. He loved her and didn't want to lose her, but she had no idea about the drug world and the addiction he was living with, day in, day out. If he could quit tomorrow, he would, but it wasn't that easy. Just thinking about the withdrawals turned his stomach into knots. The last time he tried to quit—when he first met Tammy—he was violently sick for days on end. He had called her and told her he had the flu. Once he got a fix a few hours later, he was instantly well again and hadn't tried to quit since.

He couldn't explain to her that, because of her fuck-up, he now had to pay Rick back five grand in lieu of the heroin she'd thrown away. And now he'd have to front more stuff from Rick just to keep himself well. Unsure how he was going to sort out the mess he was now in, he decided buying some time until he had an opportunity to really think things through was the best solution. "Sure, Tammy, whatever you want," he said, smiling.

CHAPTER 36

*A*nxious to start her quest to find employment, Tammy woke early the next morning. Careful not to wake Steven, she snuck quietly into the main house to take a shower. After applying her makeup, she dressed professionally in navy slacks and a white long-sleeved shirt.

When she returned to the trailer, she found Steven still sleeping. Not wanting to disturb him, she left him a note on the kitchen counter, asking him to wish her luck and telling him she'd be back later that day—hopefully with a job. She grabbed her car keys from the small table, took twenty bucks out of his jean pocket and left.

She figured a waitress job would be the easiest to find. There were many restaurants in the area and she had the right experience. She also liked the idea of the daily tips to top up her paycheck. Not knowing the roads too well, she pulled out of the driveway, drove down the street and turned left onto the main road, following it south. Her plan was to stop at every restaurant she saw and ask if they were hiring.

Five restaurants later, she was becoming discouraged. Each had told her to fill out an application and that they would call her if anything came up. Having no phone of her own, she'd left Rick's number hoping he would give her the message if they ever got in touch.

By three o'clock, Tammy had lost count on how many restaurants she'd stopped at and how many forms she'd filled out. Desperation was beginning to sink in. Just when she feared she was fast running out of time and options, she spotted a shopping center on her left and pulled into the parking lot out front. It didn't look like the sort of location where she'd find any restaurants, but she slowly scanned all the businesses from left to right, reading all the names out loud one by one. To her surprise, she spotted one called Connie's Diner. "Yes! Might as well give that one a try." She shut off the engine, grabbed her purse and exited the car.

Tammy entered the lobby with her fingers secretly crossed behind her back. It was now after three, so the lunch rush was over and the restaurant was fairly quiet. Soft guitar music played in the background and scenic pictures of harbors and lighthouses hung in neat rows on the walls. A few feet away, a pretty young blond stood behind a hostess station organizing menus. She looked up and smiled as Tammy approached.

"Table for one?" the girl asked.

"Er, actually no. I was wondering if I could speak to the manager."

The girl returned the menus to a slot at the side of her desk. "One moment please," she said before disappearing into the bar area behind her.

Tammy waited nervously by the hostess station, her palms sweating and her skin itching while she silently prayed they were hiring. A few minutes later, the girl returned, smiled, and gestured for Tammy to follow her. "Right this way please," she said with a professional tone. Tammy nodded and followed, giving her hair a quick comb with her fingers.

It was a small room with six round tables, each with four

chairs. Mirrored walls behind the bar reflected the rows of bottled liquors. Sitting on one of the eight bar stools was a short, chubby woman who looked to be of Latino descent. Surrounded by mounds of receipts and fully engaged with a calculator, she hadn't heard them enter.

"Connie, this is the lady that wishes to see you," the hostess said as they approached her. "If you need anything, I'll be out front," she added before leaving.

The woman removed her glasses, placed them on the counter, and gave Tammy the once-over.

Brushing aside her nerves, Tammy extended her hand. "Hi, I'm Tammy."

Connie took her hand and noticed right away she had a good firm grip. "Hi, I'm Connie, the owner. What can I do for you?"

"I was wondering if you were hiring."

Connie pushed the receipts aside. "Here, have a seat. Would you like a soda or something?"

Surprised by her friendliness and feeling more at ease, Tammy sat on the stool next to her. "Sure, a Coke sounds good. Thank you."

Connie left her seat to pour Tammy a drink from the soda fountain. "So, what kind of work are you looking for?"

"Well, I was hoping for a waitress position."

Connie grabbed a napkin and placed it in front of Tammy with the drink on top. "Have you had any experience?"

After taking a sip of the refreshing fizzy drink, Tammy answered, "Yes, I have. I worked in a hotel in Lonesridge, California."

Connie leaned back against the bar and casually folded her arms across her chest. "I like your accent. Where're you from?"

"I'm originally from the north of England, where I was also a waitress. From there, I moved to California." Still able to hide her pregnancy, Tammy decided not to mention it as part of her life story.

"What brought you to Seattle?"

Tammy hesitated. "My boyfriend's job."

"Ah, I see," Connie replied, returning to her seat. "Well, it just so happens..." She paused and smiled. "I had a waitress quit on me just this morning. Your timing couldn't be more perfect. I'm willing to give you a try."

Elated and feeling relieved that her search for a job had finally come to an end, Tammy was unable to contain her excitement and gratitude. She jumped up from her stool to give Connie a tremendous hug, almost knocking her off her seat in the process. "Thank you! Thank you so much!" Tammy squealed.

Amused by her excitement and having seen this kind of reaction many times before, Connie welcomed her embrace. "Now, keep in mind this is just a trial run. Let's see how you do. If you say you have the experience, then there shouldn't be a problem and the job will be yours," she said, peeling herself free of Tammy's arms.

"I won't let you down. I promise," Tammy assured her, smiling from ear to ear.

"I just need you to fill out an application with all your contact information and your social security number. I'll have Stacey at the front desk bring you one. How about you come in tomorrow for the breakfast and lunch shift and we'll see how it goes."

"That's sounds great. What time should I be here?"

"I need you here by six in the morning. I'll have a uniform ready for you. You can pick it up at the front desk."

"Okay, thank you," Tammy answered, excitement still lingering in her voice.

Connie liked her. She liked her enthusiasm and hoped she'd be a good waitress. "Okay then, I'll see you in the morning," Connie said, extending her hand.

Tammy grasped Connie's hand and shook it with every ounce of enthusiasm in her body. "I can't thank you enough for this opportunity. Again, thank you!"

"Don't thank me yet." Connie chuckled. "Show me what a great waitress you are first. Then you can thank me." She motioned with her hand pointing to the lobby. "Now, go tell Stacey to give you the application. When you're done, you can just leave it with her and I'll see you in the morning."

"Thanks, I will." Tammy trotted away to go find Stacey.

Fifteen minutes later, she pulled into the driveway behind the trailer that she reluctantly called home. "This job is going to get us out of this dump once and for all," she said before exiting the car. In a joyous mood, she skipped all the way to the trailer door, excited to tell Steven her good news. She swung the door wide open and leaped inside, yelling, "Steven!"

Standing in the living room, she quickly scanned around the small space before her eyes came to rest at the couch. In an instant, her excitement was absorbed and replaced by disappointment, sadness and anger. Steven was sprawled on the couch, sleeping. Groaning in disgust, Tammy threw her purse onto the floor, marched over to him and nudged her fist firmly on his arm, causing him to stir.

"Steven? For Christ's sake, Steven, wake up," she yelled. Still not awake, she nudged him again. "Steven!"

When he opened his eyes, Tammy's suspicions were confirmed; by his dark, dilated pupils. He was on drugs.

"Hey, baby, you're home," he slurred. "I was just taking a nap."

Tammy stood over him and glared at him with nothing but hatred oozing out of every pore of her body. She fixed her hands on her hips and snarled at him. "Oh, don't give me that crap. You're high. You were supposed to be out looking for a job like I was. You make me sick, Steven!"

He propped himself up on wobbly elbows as he struggled to bring himself up to a sitting position. Tammy watched, repulsed, while he strained to keep his eyes open and fought to keep his head up—just like he had a few nights before.

"Now hang on a second, baby, the day's not over yet. I still have time," he garbled in a sleepy tone.

"You can't go anywhere in the state you're in, and I can't stand to even look at you. Just go back to sleep. I'm leaving." But, before she could finish, he'd crumpled back on the couch in a heap and was fast asleep once again.

Feeling her skin flush a shade of red from anger, Tammy stared at the lifeless figure slumped on the sofa. She no longer felt pity for him, just repugnance. He wasn't going to take her down with him. Steven was making empty promises; she knew that now. Might he change once the baby is born? She wondered. As much as she hated him at that moment, she wasn't ready to give up on him just yet. She decided she would give him the chance to prove himself and show her that he could be a good father to their child.

CHAPTER 37

Over the next few months, Tammy worked as many hours as she possibly could. Sometimes, she picked up extra shifts by covering for the other waitresses, which earned her a little extra money. By buying just the necessities, Tammy managed to save some money—without Steven's knowledge, of course. With the trust gone, she hid her savings in a coffee can that she kept buried in the yard.

She was now almost seven months pregnant, but because she was tall and had gained little weight, she had been successful in hiding it. Being on her feet all day was beginning to take its toll on her already exhausted body, but she continued to push herself, knowing she had only two more months to find an apartment before the baby arrived.

To Tammy's dismay, Steven made no efforts to change and continued to not only use but also sell heroin. They were living under the same roof but leading separate lives. She left him to his despicable lifestyle and refused to take any of his drug money, no matter how broke she was. Her only hope was that he would change once the baby was born. She continued to work hard, determined to get them out of the trailer as quickly as possible; she accomplished her goal just six weeks before her due date and felt triumphant about her success.

In between her shifts, Tammy spent her time scanning the classifieds and had found a one-bedroom apartment just five minutes from work. It was going to be tough, especially because she wasn't counting on any help from Steven. She had enough money saved for the down payment and the first month's rent, but little money for anything else. She was told they could move into the apartment in two days. Unfortunately, it wasn't furnished, but it did have a refrigerator and a stove, which was a start. She could shop at the local thrift stores for the other things they needed, and little by little, just like she had with their last apartment and even the trailer, she would make it a home. Not for Steven, but for the baby.

After signing the lease, Tammy stopped at a few stores in search of boxes and brought home a car full. She wanted to start packing right away. Although she hadn't yet told Steven about their impending move, she was quite sure he wouldn't object to leaving that horrible trailer.

With not much to pack other than clothes, books, and toiletries, Tammy had most of it done by the early evening. She stacked the completed boxes neatly in the front room. Within minutes of taping up the last box and standing back to admire her work, she heard Rick's van pull up in the driveway. Tammy listened to them chatting outside but couldn't make out what they were saying until Steven said, "Night, man," and walked toward their door.

With butterflies fluttering in her stomach, Tammy stood in the kitchen and patiently waited for the door to open. She watched in silence as he entered and stopped in his tracks at the sight of the pile of boxes. "What's this?" he asked, a puzzled look creeping over his face.

Refusing to fear him, she stood tall with her back straight and proudly made the announcement. "We're moving. We can finally be rid of this bloody trailer. I found us an apartment, and I only hope you're as excited as I am." The look on his face told her right away he wasn't.

"Moving? Why? We live here for free."

His pathetic reasoning astounded her. "As I've told you many times before, I'm not raising our baby in a caravan, Steven. Or a bloody *trailer* as you call it. I found us a nice apartment close to my work, and if you get a real job, we'll be able to afford it comfortably."

Steven took a seat on the couch and crossed one foot over his knee. "Don't you think we should have talked about this first? I'm not ready to move."

"This isn't about you, Steven, it's about the baby. How can you be so goddamn selfish?" Tammy threw him a sarcastic laugh. "I actually thought you'd be excited about getting out of here. Instead, you're giving me stupid, lame excuses, and I can't figure out why."

"I can't just move, Tammy," Steven said defensively.

"Why not? I did when we left California, remember?" Tammy folded her arms and huffed. "You don't have to do a bloody thing except load the boxes into the car. I've already paid the rent and packed everything up, and I've already been told we can move in the day after tomorrow. What possible reason do you have for not wanting to leave?"

"What about Rick?"

"What about Rick? You don't need his fucking permission."

"I work for the guy. I can't just leave," Steven protested, raising his voice slightly.

Frustrated, Tammy yelled back louder, "Yes, you can. Selling drugs isn't a *job*; it's a crime for God's sake! Moving now will give you enough time to find a real job and get away from all this crap." Tammy shook her head in disbelief. "I can't believe I'm having to talk you into leaving this pit-hole."

Steven mulled over in his head all the things he couldn't tell

Tammy. He depended on the gig with Rick, not only to make some money but also to get his fixes. He wasn't ready to quit. He had to prepare himself to be gradually weaned down. He had to psyche himself up to face months, if not years of living hell as he transitioned through the painful phases of withdrawal. He needed time. Otherwise, he felt he might as well just kill himself there and then.

"Let me think about it. Okay?"

Tammy couldn't contain her fury. "Think about it? What's there to fucking think about? The place is ours. Tell you what, Steven, you can *think about it* all you fucking want, but I'm moving in. You can stay in this dump if you want. I don't care. I'm getting the hell out of here." She yanked her purse from the counter, flung it over her shoulder and stormed toward the door. "I'm going for a walk. While I'm gone, why don't you ask yourself, Steven...what's more important? Your fucking drugs or your child?"

"Wait, Tammy," he pleaded as she opened the door to leave.

"No! I need to get out of here. I can't believe you're saying you have to think about this." Without looking back, she stomped out of the trailer and slammed the door behind her.

Steven sat in despair, knowing full well his world was falling apart. No matter what he decided to do, he was about to lose the two most important things in his life—Tammy and his child. He loved her so much, and yet he knew how much he was hurting her at the same time. If he left Rick's, he could probably get enough stuff to tide him over for a week, but after that, the violent withdrawals would begin. Tammy would never be able to handle it; she'd freak out and probably leave. And, if he stayed at Rick's, then he'd already lost her.

CHAPTER 38

*W*ith so many uncertainties of what lay ahead, Steven reluctantly moved into the new apartment with Tammy. He couldn't abandon her and the baby. He had done some really shitty things already, so she didn't deserve to have to deal with that too. Rick had given him enough stash to get by for about a week, but only if he controlled his uses and made it last. What he would do after that week concerned him the most.

Steven watched as Tammy skipped and twirled in a joyous dance around their empty apartment, spreading her arms out wide as she shrieked and squealed with delight. When she passed by him, she beamed him a glorious smile—something he had missed more than he realized. It warmed his heart to see her happy again. Unable to match her enthusiasm, he idly leaned against the wall of the hallway and chuckled as she whisked by him again, this time on her way to check out the bathroom and the bedroom.

"This is perfect for us," Tammy squeaked like a little child. "We'll have it fixed up in no time. Just in time for the baby. I have so many ideas," she said, still beaming a smile. "There are some really good thrift stores around here. I bet we can find a lot of stuff there. What do you think?"

"Sounds great, honey."

Suddenly, Tammy had an idea. "Hey, you know what. I don't have to be at work for a couple more hours. Let's go to the thrift store now!" she suggested.

Steven wasn't feeling up to it; he could feel the stuff wearing off, but he had to hold it together for a few more hours. Maybe shopping would help take his mind off it. "Sure, we can do that."

"Oh wait, we still have a few more boxes in the car. Can you grab them?"

Steven knew he didn't have the strength to carry the boxes up to their second-floor apartment. Not without taking a fix early. He'd make up the time with the next one, he convinced himself. "Yeah, okay, but let me use the bathroom first."

Tammy suspected he was going to use drugs but avoided questioning him. She didn't want anything to spoil her mood. "Okay, I'll wait for you."

～

Over the next few weeks, Tammy diligently saved money to buy furnishings for the apartment, including a couch, a television, and a dining room table and four chairs. She bought pictures for the walls and filled the kitchen with cookware, dishes, and silverware.

But the brief happiness she'd experienced with Steven deteriorated rapidly as the novelty of their new apartment began to wear off. The trust still wasn't there. Obsessed, wondering if he was still using, Tammy found herself constantly looking for evidence. She'd look closely at his eyes to see if they were dilated, knowing now that dilated pupils were a common sign. She'd watch him walk across the room, waiting for him to stumble. If he sat down, she'd stare at him out of the corner of her eye to see if he nodded off. As part of her daily routine, she'd search all the cabinets, under the bed, and down the sides of the couch cushions for drug paraphernalia, needles, tar, cotton balls, or spoons. Surprisingly, she found none, but she convinced herself it was because she just hadn't found his hiding spot yet.

The times his body language told her he was high; Tammy chose to say nothing. Now in her third trimester, she didn't want the added stress of fighting a losing battle. Fearing his anger, she'd reasoned that silence was the best solution. She needed to get through the pregnancy first. Then she'd figure out what to do. So far, her pregnancy had been an easy one. She'd had no morning sickness and had only gained twelve pounds, which allowed her to remain active and keep on at work. The doctors were not concerned about her lack of weight gain; they reassured her the baby was doing fine and seemed healthy. Because she was tall—almost six feet—the pregnancy still wasn't showing as anything beyond a slight bump, which could easily be hidden with a baggier shirt, so she hadn't felt the need to confide in anyone at work that she was expecting.

Tammy's suspicions of Steven's drug use were confirmed when he came home in a frantic state one day and demanded twenty dollars from her. When she refused, he charged at her with a vengeance and cornered her in the kitchen, his body trembling with anger, his pale face highlighted with blotches of red creeping up from his neck. Tammy, afraid he may strike out at her if she didn't, caved in and handed him the money. Within seconds, he fled through the door, leaving Tammy drenched in her own tears.

When he returned later that day, wearing his signature smirk, he apologized profoundly and promised it would never happen again.

But, it did—just two days later. It was the beginning of a vicious cycle.

Steven's addiction was spiraling out of control. No longer on easy street with Rick, the hunt for the drug consumed him from morning till night. Having a two-hundred-dollar-a-day habit, his days were spent stealing all kinds of merchandise, finding buyers for stolen goods, cashing in, and then—the ultimate reward—buying the drug.

Tammy was now living with a complete stranger. The once happy, funny, and loving Steven had been replaced by a person that repulsed her. A man, that had no dignity or ambition. His long, matted hair acted as a daily reminder that Steven no longer had any pride. His clothes hung like rags from his skeletal frame, and his skin, the color of a corpse, showed what a sick man he was. No one could help or save him; this was his battle, not hers.

The thought of returning to her father's had crossed her mind on more than one occasion since moving into the new apartment, but an unexpected phone call crushed that idea before it even had chance to get off the ground. Her dad broke the news that he and Joanne were moving to Florida at the end of the month and may also be living in Ireland for part of the year. The thought of both parents being thousands of miles away made Tammy nervous and, for the first time, she experienced a sense of utter loneliness. She had too much pride to ask her father for help. It was up to her to somehow find a way to break loose from Steven once the baby was born so she could give her child the life it deserved.

After working late one night, covering a cocktail shift, Tammy returned home exhausted only to find Steven passed out on the couch. Sickened by the sight of him, she simply shook her head and left him in his drugged-out state before going to bed alone.

She tossed and turned for hours, experiencing severe stomach cramps that prevented her from getting off to sleep. Frustrated, she glanced at the illuminated clock and saw it was three in the morning. "Damn it!" she barked while reaching over to turn on the bedside lamp. She threw back the blankets in a fit of annoyance and grabbed her bathrobe from the end of the bed. Tugging aggressively at the ties, she wrapped herself in the pink terry-cloth robe and headed to the kitchen to get a glass of water.

But she only managed to make it as far as the bedroom door before she felt a warm gush of fluids run down her legs. Instantly, she knew her water had broken and the baby was coming. Holding onto the door handle for support, she bent over in excruciating pain as she experienced her first contraction. "Oh my god!" she yelled in agony, hoping it would soon pass.

With the pain subsiding, Tammy fumbled to open the door and yelled down the hallway, "Steven! The baby is coming!" There was no response. She waited for the contraction to fully pass and, while grasping her stomach and using the walls for balance, she slowly made her way down the hall. When she reached the front room, she flicked on the lights. Steven was not on the couch. She looked down and saw he had rolled off and was now passed out on the floor. In desperation and unable to bend down, she fought her pain and kicked him in the gut. "Steven, wake up. The baby is coming."

"Ouch! What the fuck," he yelled, placing a limp hand over his stomach.

"Get up, Steven. I need you to drive me to the hospital. I'm in labor."

"Oh shit!" In an instant, he suddenly appeared normal and sober. Dragging his fingers through his hair, he jumped to his feet in a frenzy and began to walk circles around the room. "What do we do?"

"First, I need you to calm down. Then I need you to get my overnight bag from the bedroom while I call the midwife."

"Okay." Without another word, he hurried off to retrieve the bag while Tammy stumbled for the phone.

With a fear of drugs embedded in her, all thanks to Steven's usage, Tammy had chosen in advance to deliver by natural child-birth. Like the rest of her pregnancy, the delivering went smoothly and quickly with no complications. Just two hours after her first contraction, she gave birth to a beautiful baby boy, weighing in at seven pounds, four ounces.

Surprisingly, Steven stuck around during the delivery, holding Tammy's hand and telling her to breathe during the contractions. But, as soon as the baby was swaddled in her arms, he made an excuse to leave. Tammy knew the real reason why he had to abandon her and his newborn child less than twenty minutes after welcoming him into the world, but she let him go without protest.

When he returned, the signature smirk confirmed what he'd needed the bathroom for. He might be high, but Tammy wasn't going to let anything spoil the magical moment she was experiencing. Bonding with her son cradled in her arms, she was already madly in love and totally amazed by his perfection. Up until that moment, she had not thought of a name, but now, as she looked down on him, the name suddenly came to her. Tammy smiled and kissed his tiny forehead. "Hi, Matt."

"Who's Matt?" Steven asked.

"Our son. I'm naming him Matt. Not as in Matt, short for Matthew, just Matt, and his name is not up for debate."

Steven didn't argue. "I like it. It's fine with me."

Tammy gave her new son a little squeeze. "Isn't he beautiful?"

Steven stroked Matt's full head of black hair. "He sure is." He then looked at Tammy and smiled. "I'm going to be a good dad. You watch."

It meant nothing to her. She'd heard his promises too many times before, all of which had been broken. "Don't just say it, Steven. Show me. The most important thing in my life now is this little boy. If you can't be there for him, we'll be just fine on our own. I mean it, Steven. I'm not going to subject him to a life surrounded by drugs and crime."

Looking down at his son, Steven knew he was in serious jeopardy of losing them both. He couldn't let that happen. He needed help and he needed it fast.

CHAPTER 39

"What do you mean you had a baby? You weren't pregnant last night."

Tammy giggled down the phone. "I'm sorry I never told you, Connie. I was afraid you wouldn't hire me if you knew. And I was able to hide it pretty well. I'm sorry I'm laughing, but I would love to see your face right now."

"No, I just don't believe you. Listen, I know you worked late last night...if you're tired, girl, just let me know and I'll give you the day off. But don't lie to me."

Again, Tammy laughed. "Connie, I'm serious. I'm not lying. I had a baby boy less than three hours ago. There's no way I can come into work today. If you don't believe me, I'm at Northwest Hospital. Come down and meet our new son Matt."

"I think I'll just do that. I'll see you soon! Bye for now," she said with uncertainty and hung up.

Within the hour, Connie was by Tammy's bedside and chattering away with baby talk to Matt. Tammy was happy Steven had left. She probably wouldn't see him for the rest of the day, and she needed to talk to Connie anyway.

"Where did you hide him, girl? He's so precious. I can't believe I didn't know. You're going to have to take some time off. How much do you need?"

"Actually, I kinda wanted to talk to you about that."

Connie, was all ears. "Sure. What's up?"

"Well, Steven isn't working right now and money is tight. If I can find a sitter, I want to come back to work in the next couple of days. I feel great so I'm sure I'll be fine."

Connie had grown close to Tammy over the last few months. She wasn't sure what was going on, but she had an intuition that it wasn't all roses at home for Tammy. "Well, maybe I can I help."

"You? How?"

"Well, you know I live above the restaurant. I could watch the little guy there while you're working. And, not only that, I must confess that I absolutely love babies." Connie chuckled while gently squeezing Matt's cheek.

Tammy was surprised by her gesture. "Oh, Connie, I can't ask you to watch Matt for me, it's just—."

"You didn't ask. I'm offering." "I...I don't know what to say. Thank you!"

Connie patted Tammy's shoulder lovingly. "No need to thank me. I'll put you on breakfast and lunch so you can be at home with him in the evenings."

"That would be great, thank you. I really don't know what I'd do without you."

～

Tammy did what she intended to do and returned to work just two days after giving birth to Matt. With no help from Steven— whose days were still consumed by drugs—she couldn't afford not to.

By the end of the month, after working as much as she could, Tammy felt she had failed her son. Despite saving as much money as possible, she only had half the month's rent and was going berserk with worry as she contemplated what to do. She returned home, feeling utterly exhausted, and laid her sleeping son in the middle of her bed before straightening his blankets and putting him into his crib.

Satisfied that he was safe and sound asleep, she turned toward his crib and pulled back the small mattress. She let out a sigh of relief; Steven hadn't found it. Tammy retrieved the white envelope she had stashed and slid it open with her finger. To her absolute horror, she discovered it was empty. "No...No...NO!"

In disbelief, Tammy checked the envelope again. She shook it and turned it upside down. It was empty. She gently slid her hand under the mattress to check it hadn't slipped out. Nothing. Steven had found her stash and taken the money she had been saving for rent. Shaking uncontrollably, she fell to her knees and sobbed. "How could he? How could he do this to us? What am I going to do now?" Crying, Tammy crawled over to Matt and gathered him in her arms, being careful not to wake him. With soft kisses to his forehead, she spoke to him in a soft, comforting voice. "It'll be okay, Matt. I'll take care of you. I love you so much. I'll figure something out, I promise."

Later that night, unable to sleep with worry, Tammy heard the front door open and close. She glanced at the clock illuminating the darkened room and saw it was just after midnight. She ripped the bed covers away from her body, leaped out of bed, and charged down the hallway into the living room in a rage.

She turned on the lights and found Steven standing in the middle of the room, swaying from side to side. Inching closer to him and seeing his eyes were closed, she watched as he struggled to hold his head up. Tammy knew instantly; he was high.

He turned his head with what looked like an almighty effort and gazed at her through half-open, sunken eyes. "Hey, honey," he slurred. "I didn't know you were up."

In a fury, Tammy marched toward him until she was within an

inch of his spaced-out face. "How could you!" she yelled, shoving him backwards as hard as she could.

From the force of her unexpected push, Steven lost his balance and fell onto the couch behind him, where he erupted into a fit of giggles.

"How could I what?" he mumbled in a squeaky voice, seeming to assume Tammy was playing some sort of game.

Tammy took a step back as Steven struggled to his feet in front of her. "You've stolen the money I had stashed away. That was for our fucking rent, Steven!" she screamed, feeling her anger intensify. "I hate you!" She raised her hand and slapped him hard across his cheek. Her hand stung, but it felt good to blast her rage at him.

Steven's head whipped around, causing him to fall back onto the couch again. Rubbing the red mark that was now forming on his face, he hollered back, "Fuck! I'm sorry, okay. I was sick. I just happened to stumble across the envelope and temptation got the better of me."

"You didn't *stumble* on that money. You hunted high and low for it until you found it. I'm sick of your fucking lies!" Tammy hollered before kicking the sole of her foot into his shin.

Steven winced and leaned forward to rub his leg. "Goddammit! Quit hitting me, okay. I said I was sorry. Let's talk about this in the morning. I'll get the money back."

Tammy let out a sarcastic laugh. "You'll get the money back, will you? You're a fucking loser, Steven. I used to feel sorry for you, but now, I totally despise you and I just can't wait till I'm free of you."

In an instant, Steven was alert. Taking Tammy by surprise, he grabbed her arm and pulled her down within inches of his face while squeezing her arm tight and digging his nails into her skin.

Tammy shuddered with fear as her body tensed up from the pain.

With a piercing stare, he growled, "If you ever try to leave me and take my son away from me, Tammy, believe me, I will find you. I will hunt you down and you'll wish you never had." He tightened his grip around her arm. "Do you understand me?"

Tammy winched from the pain. "Yes," she whimpered, uncertain of what he might do if she tried to argue.

Steven released his grip, leaned back against the couch and smirked.

"Good. Do we understand each other now?"

Tammy rubbed her arm to ease the throbbing pain spreading over her skin. "Yes, we do." Wanting only the comfort of her son, she ran down the hallway with tears swelling in her eyes. Closing the door behind her, she let the tears fall. Through her watery eyes, she looked down at Matt innocently sleeping in his crib. She was relieved to find their shouting hadn't woken him.

Seeing the rage in Steven's eyes when he threatened her had made her realize he was more than capable of harming her. But would he hurt his own son?

CHAPTER 40

The next morning, Tammy was woken by the sound of Steven's stern voice while he shook her arm. "Come on, get up. We're going to my mother's house."

"What?" she asked, still in a sleepy state.

"You heard me. We're going to my mother's." He ripped the covers away from her body. "So, get up and just grab what we need."

"I can't just leave! What about my job?"

"You'll get another."

"But your mother lives in Los Angeles!" She heard Matt stirring in the crib and got up from the bed. "Out of my way. Matt's waking up," Tammy said while gesturing with her hands for Steven to move aside. She picked up Matt and rocked him in her arms. "So, we're going to run away again? Leave everything behind again? That's your plan?" she asked, her voice laced with sarcasm.

"Well, do you have a better one? My mother will put us up for a while, and besides, it's about time she met her grandson, don't you think?"

After last night, she didn't want to piss him off—especially in front of Matt. "Fine, I'll start packing after I've fed Matt."

"Good. I'm going out for a while. I'll be back in a couple hours. I want you and Matt ready to leave when I get back."

Knowing he'd probably left to score drugs with the rent money he'd stolen, it crossed Tammy's mind to leave with Matt while he was gone. But he had taken her car, and she feared the consequences of being found if she tried to escape. For now, she'd have to go along with his plan. She would know when the time was right to leave.

While sitting in the rocking chair feeding Matt, Tammy made the difficult phone call to Connie. After two rings, a female voice answered the restaurant's phone. Tammy recognized it as the hostess, Stacey. "Connie's Diner. How may I help you?"

"Hi, Stacey, it's Tammy. Is Connie available?"

"Hey, Tammy. One second, let me transfer you to the bar."

"Thanks." Tammy listened to a moment of soothing classical music while her call was transferred.

"Hello, Connie speaking."

"Hey, Connie, it's Tammy."

"Hi, Tammy. How's my little man?"

"He's fine. Listen, I hate to tell you this with such short notice..." She hesitated and took a deep breath. "I won't be able to work for you anymore. I feel awful about it, Connie, and I'm so sorry. You've been so good to me."

"Is everything okay?" Connie asked, concerned.

Tammy lied. "Yes, everything's fine. Steven's mother is sick, so we're going to move in with her for a while so he can take care of her. She lives in Los Angeles."

Connie wasn't buying her story but didn't want to intervene. "I'm so sorry. I'm going to miss you, but I'm going to miss little Matt even more."

"I know, I'm going to miss you too, Connie. Is it okay if I come in later today and pick up my final check?"

"Sure, I'll have it ready for you. And, Tammy?"

"Yes?"

"If you ever need anything, I'm here."

Tammy read between the lines perfectly well and knew she was reaching out, but she couldn't possibly involve Connie in her twisted world. "Thanks, I will." She sighed and hung up the phone.

Tammy knew she should probably call her dad and Joanne with the disturbing news that she was moving yet again. But, not knowing the address of Steven's mother, she decided against it. She didn't have any answers to the concerning questions they'd probably have. Once she was settled, she'd call them with the same excuse she gave Connie.

Once Matt had fallen asleep, she placed him in his crib and began to pack.

CHAPTER 41

wo days later, Tammy and Steven pulled into an apartment complex in San Gabriel, a suburb of Los Angeles.

"Wow, I haven't been here in over five years but it still looks the same," Steven said as he parked the car and opened his door.

Tammy stepped out, opened the back door, and lifted Matt out of his car seat. "Can you grab the diaper bag from the trunk? I need to change him," Tammy asked, her voice flat.

Once they had what they needed, Tammy followed Steven through a narrow passageway toward the apartments. Straight away, Tammy noticed the white metal bars on all the windows. "What's with all the bars? It's like living in a jail."

"It's to stop people from breaking in," Steven answered.

"Can't be a very good neighborhood if you have to bar up your windows."

"It's fine, Tammy. My mom's lived here for over fifteen years and has never had a problem. Why do you always have to find fault with everything?"

"I'm not finding fault. I was merely observing. It's the first place I've ever seen with bars on the windows. That's all."

He shook his head. "Whatever."

Steven approached apartment number 102 on the first floor and banged on the metal screen door, causing it to shake and make a rattling noise.

"Steven! Not so loud," Tammy hissed. "She's hard of hearing. It's you that needs to be quiet. Jeez."

Tammy stood behind him holding Matt, nervously anticipating meeting his mother for the first time. A few moments later, the door behind the screen opened and a frail old lady, using a cane to steady herself, peered through the mesh.

"Hi, Ma, it's Steven!" he yelled.

The old lady looked confused. "Steven?"

"Yes, it's me. Open the door."

His mother fiddled with a few locks and latches on the inside of the door and finally managed to unlock it. Both Tammy and Steven took a step back as she pushed it open toward them. Tammy was astonished by her age; she had to be at least seventy. Then, Tammy remembered Steven telling her she'd had him when she was forty-five.

"Ma!" Steven bellowed, pulling Tammy in closer to him, causing Tammy to cringe. "This is my girlfriend Tammy, and this is your grandson Matt."

Unable to hide her look of shock caused by their unannounced visit, Steven's mother clasped her bony frail hands in front of her face. Tammy noticed the prominent purple veins crisscrossing her skin like a web. "Oh my goodness! Hi, Tammy, I'm Elizabeth. Come in."

"Hi," Tammy said softly with a kind smile.

Following Steven inside, Tammy saw it was a simple two-bedroom apartment, darkened by the closed drapes. Every available surface was cluttered with dusty knick-knacks and photos.

Gaudy, gold framed pictures of flowers and fruit bowls hung from almost every inch of the walls.

Tammy settled herself on the burgundy couch with Matt and watched with pity as Elizabeth struggled to sit next to her. Every movement seemed to cause her discomfort and pain. Tammy turned to Steven, who seemed oblivious to his mother's troubles, and whispered with disbelieving sarcasm. "Will you help her? I can't believe I have to ask you to help your own mother."

Dumbfounded by her request and feeling awkward at the idea of having to help his ailing mother, he complied reluctantly and steadied her with a hand on her arm as she slowly lowered herself onto the couch.

"Oh, he is so precious," Elizabeth, said, staring into her grandson's eyes. "Why didn't you call me and let me know you were coming? I would have fixed us something to eat."

"We wanted to surprise you, Ma." Steven paused. "In fact, we were thinking about staying for a few days." He looked over at Tammy. "Right, Tammy?" he asked with a persistent tone.

Tammy looked away from his stare and turned to his mother. "Err, yes, if it's okay with you, Elizabeth. We don't want to impose on you."

Before Elizabeth could answer, Steven had left the matching burgundy chair and was at his mother's side. He placed a gentle hand on her shoulder. "It's no trouble. Is it, Ma? You want to spend time with your grandson, don't you, Ma?" His leering smile made Tammy shift uncomfortably in her seat.

His mother reached up and patted her son's hand. "Of course I do. You can stay here for as long as you want. You can have the spare bedroom. You may have to clean it up a bit, I've not been in there for quite some time."

Tammy felt sorry for her. She seemed so frail and lost. Steven didn't seem at all concerned about his mother's failing health, only with what she could give him. Shelter, food, and—most importantly, Tammy assumed—money. "Don't you worry about it, Elizabeth. I'll be happy to clean the room," Tammy said.

"Are you sure?" Steven's mother asked.

"Yes, I'm sure. It's the least I can do." Tammy gave her a friendly smile. "And thank you."

Within less than twenty-four hours, Tammy witnessed Steven coaxing money from his elderly mother. Whatever stories he told her were probably lies but, from that day forward, his mother gave him cash every morning. With money in his hand and a smirk on his face, he left, not to be seen until after dark. Insisting the car be left with her because of Matt, Tammy would stare from the kitchen window, which looked out onto the main street, and watch Steven jump into a black beat-up sedan before speeding off down the street.

His mother was oblivious to his drug use. He was an only child, and in the eyes of a mother, her son could do no wrong. Tammy was afraid to tell her, knowing it would break her heart.

Left alone all day with Matt, Tammy soon became friends with Elizabeth's neighbor, Natalie, who was a stay-at-home mom with two young boys aged two and three. They frequently spent the afternoons together in the courtyard, letting her two boys play while Matt got some sun and fresh air. Some days, Natalie watched Matt for a couple of hours while Tammy looked for work. After a week of searching, she found a job as a waitress at a local diner.

Thrilled for Tammy, Natalie relieved one of Tammy's biggest concerns and offered to watch Matt while she was at work.

That night, while Elizabeth and Matt were sleeping, Tammy told Steven about her successful job hunt. As usual, he'd arrived home well after ten o'clock wearing the smirk she despised. After a quick "hi," he grabbed a beer from the fridge, took a seat on the couch, stretched his legs out on the coffee table and fixed his eyes on the television.

Dressed in her bathrobe, Tammy sat in the chair across from

him. "I thought you should know I got a job today. I start tomorrow."

"Why?" He asked, not taking his eyes off the TV.

"Well, we can't stay here forever. I don't want your mum supporting us. Don't you feel bad taking money from her every day?"

Steven laughed. "It's not that much. Besides, she loves me."

Tammy hated his cocky laugh. "Well, it bothers me. I want to contribute."

Steven steered his eyes away from the television. "Who's going to watch Matt? Surely not my mother?"

"No! I wouldn't dream of asking her. I've become friends with Natalie next door. Not that you would know, being away all day. Anyway, she's going to watch him."

"Well, it looks like you got it all figured out. Does this mean you'll get tips every day?"

Tammy could tell he was mulling something through in his head but wasn't going to ask. Whatever it was, it wouldn't be good. "Yes, and it will help with diapers and stuff for Matt." Tammy shifted in her seat. "You know, it wouldn't hurt for you to find a job. Matt is your son too, you know?"

Steven threw back his head and scrunched his eyes closed. "Oh, don't start with me, Tammy. I'm working on something. It takes time."

"You always have an excuse, don't you, Steven?" She stood up and marched towards their bedroom. "I'm off to bed." Just like she did every night, she went to bed alone feeling nothing but hate for the man in the other room.

Now that Tammy had money coming in, she desperately wanted to get Steven away from his mother before he drained her completely. Secretly, she opened a saving account, but struggled to put much away because of Steven's constant demands. Knowing she'd have tips after being on the floor for a few hours, he'd made it a daily habit to show up at her work and force her to give him all the money she had. He'd regularly back her into a corner and pin her against the wall, leaving Tammy with no choice but to give him some cash. She couldn't risk causing a scene that may result in her losing her job.

During her lunch break one day, she scoured the classifieds for apartments but found they were all well out of her price range. Feeling discouraged, even more so by the pouring rain, she finished her shift, grabbed a newspaper to shield her head, and made a dash for her car.

A few blocks away, Tammy was surprised to see one of her co-workers, Judy, standing at a bus stop with no umbrella or hat. She quickly veered her car off to the side of the road and pulled up alongside of her. Tammy leaned over toward the passenger side of the car and rolled down the window. "Judy," she hollered. "You're getting soaked. Do you want a ride?"

Judy approached the car and peered in through the open window, her nose and cheeks flushed from the cold raindrops trickling down her face. Her flat, lifeless hair framed her face in a mangled mess. "Oh, hi, Tammy. Sure, that would be great. Thanks," Judy said with gratitude. "If you don't mind. I don't live too far from here."

Tammy reached over and pushed the door open. "Sure, no problem. Hop in."

Judy lowered herself into the dry, warm car, relieved to be out of the rain. "Thanks," she said again.

"My god, Judy, you're drenched." Tammy turned her head and searched the back seat. "I know I always keep a towel in here. I never know when I may need one, especially when my kid is riding with me." She scanned some more and then spotted the corner of it peeking out from under a bag. "Oh, here it is." With one hand, Tammy pulled it up between the two seats and handed it to Judy.

Judy smiled. "Thanks," she said and began dabbing her face.

"Where do you live?" Tammy asked while pulling away from the curb.

"Oh, not too far. About three miles down this road, at the Clifford Motel."

"You live in a motel?" Tammy questioned. "Isn't that expensive?"

"Actually, no, it isn't. I pay by the week. They never asked me for a deposit and the utilities are included."

Tammy was intrigued. "What about cooking?"

"I have a little fridge, a microwave, and a hotplate. It's amazing what you can do when you have limited space."

"Would you mind if I come take a look at your place? I've been looking for an apartment, but everything in the newspapers is so damn expensive."

"Sure, if you don't mind the mess. I have two kids so it gets kinda cramped."

Tammy couldn't hide her look of surprise. "You have two kids? I had no idea."

"Yeah, I don't talk much about my personal life at work."

Tammy understood. She, too, hadn't shared the fact that the father of her child was a drug addict, or that she was supporting him while they lived with his elderly mother in her small apartment. She wondered what else there was to know about Judy. How did she end up living in a motel? And where was the father of her children?

CHAPTER 42

A few minutes later, Judy instructed Tammy to pull up in front of a pale blue two-story building with white trims, scattered palm trees, and lush green lawns.

"This is it," Judy said as the car came to a halt.

Tammy was impressed. "It doesn't look too bad," she remarked as she got out of the car. Closely inspecting every inch of the building and grounds as she looked around, Tammy followed Judy up the pathway and through a tall metal gate.

"It's not. But it's not the best either," Judy said with a laugh.

Tammy ducked her head inside the collar of her jacket in an attempt to avoid the rain hitting her face. She liked the central courtyard with the benches and tables, even though they'd been soaked with the day's terrible weather. To the left, she spotted a gated community pool, which was unsurprisingly deserted because of the rain. Tammy envisioned it filled with sunbathing moms capturing every moment of peace while their children squealed and frolicked in the pool. Walking past the rooms, Tammy heard television sets blasting loud, children playing, couples fighting, and parents yelling at their kids. It wasn't a quiet place, Tammy noticed.

"This is a busy place," Tammy stated as they approached room number 109 on the first floor.

"Yeah, most of the people live here full time, like me. Mainly single moms and families on welfare," Judy replied while pulling out a bunch of keys from the front pocket of her uniform. She unlocked the door and motioned with her head for Tammy to go inside. As Tammy stepped through the door, Judy threw her keys down on top of the TV set and opened the drapes to let in some light. "Well, this is it. Told you it wasn't much, but it's home to me and my babies."

Tammy glanced around the small, cluttered motel room. Protruding out into the middle of the room were two unmade queen-size beds with very little space between them and much less to walk around the edges. Piled on both beds were toys, clothes, and two laundry baskets filled with towels and even more clothes. Across every surface, various items were piled on top of each other in a jumbled mess. The single sink counter was stacked high with diapers and groceries, but she spotted a microwave and a hot plate among the clutter. Beneath the counter was a small black fridge, and to the right was a closed door, which Tammy assumed was the bathroom.

Judy walked over to the sink, grabbed a towel hanging from the wall, and gently dabbed her damp hair. "Do you want a towel?" she asked.

"Nah, I'm fine. Thanks."

After giving her hair a quick brush and checking it in the mirror, Judy untied her apron and flung it on the counter. "I have to pick up my kids. Do you mind hanging out here for a bit? I'll just be a few minutes."

"Do you need a ride? It's still raining. I don't mind taking you."

"No, but thanks. My babysitter, Maria, lives here on the second floor."

"Oh, well that's convenient," Tammy remarked.

"Yeah, it sure is. Especially since I don't have a car right now." As Judy headed toward the open door, Tammy darted in between the two beds to allow her to get by.

"I won't be long. Make yourself at home."

Tammy sat on the edge of one of the beds and scoured the room, picturing her and Matt living in such a place. Funnily enough, Steven wasn't in the picture. She liked that. She thought how perfect it would be, and at least it was something she could afford on her own. She wondered about the babysitter on the premises and imagined how convenient that would be, too. If the motel had vacancies and the sitter was taking more kids, this could be a way out for her. The thought excited her. Maybe this was the solution she'd been looking for.

In less than ten minutes, Judy returned carrying a sleeping baby boy in her arms and holding the hand of a shy four-year-old girl.

"Hi, what's your name?" Tammy asked the small girl.

"Tell her your name, sweetie," Judy said, giving her daughter's hand a gentle shake.

The little girl smiled. "It's Kate."

"Hi, Kate, it's nice to meet you. My name is Tammy."

Kate hid behind her mother. "Hi, Tammy."

"And this little guy is Christopher. He just turned nine months." Tammy saw she was heading toward the bed and quickly jumped up.

"Here, let me help," Tammy said while placing the laundry baskets on the floor.

"Thanks." Judy smiled and laid her son in the middle of the bed before covering him with a blanket. "Hey, Kate, how about you play with some of your Barbies over on the floor by the sink while your brother sleeps. Okay?"

"Okay, Mommy." Kate scooped up an armful of her dolls and skipped over to her designated spot.

Tammy smiled and sat back down on one of the beds as she watched Kate organizing her dolls. "Aww, she's so cute."

Judy sat across from her next to her son. "Thanks. As you can see, it gets pretty cramped in here, but we make do."

"How long have you lived here?" Tammy asked.

"About six months."

Tammy wanted to know more. "Where's the kids' dad? Does he live here too?"

Judy looked down at her son while she spoke, rubbing his stomach gently. "No, he doesn't. He's in prison and won't be out for a while."

Tammy gasped. "In prison? For what?"

"Oh, the usual. Drugs, selling drugs, using drugs. It's not the first time. He's always in and out of jail. I'm used to it."

Astounded that her husband seemed so much like Steven, Tammy was curious and had to ask. "Why do you put up with it? Why not leave him?"

"I don't really know. I know I should, and I tell myself that every time he gets arrested and goes back inside. I just can't seem to do it. Plus, I don't want to take the kids away from their daddy. They would be heartbroken. He's not the best father, but he's all they have." And then, with a heavy sigh, she added, "And I guess, deep down, I'm hoping that the next time he gets out of jail, he'll change and start being a good husband and a better father to our kids." She paused and smiled. "Ha! I'm still waiting for that day."

Tammy detected her sarcasm. They both knew her husband was never going to change, but she continued to stay and tolerate his behavior because of the kids. Tammy felt like she was looking at her own reflection. Like Judy, she was just making excuses for Steven and it sickened her.

"But it never happens, does it?" Tammy said, looking down at her clasped hands on her lap.

"No, it doesn't," Judy replied, unable to hide the disappointment in her voice. "But I keep holding onto that dream," she added, her eyes now misty.

"You know, I can relate to what you're going through," Tammy said, reaching out and gently patting Judy's leg.

"You can?" Is your husband in jail too?"

"No, but it's just a matter of time." Tammy paused briefly, wondering whether or not to disclose any more. "I've never told anyone this before. I think it's because I've never met anyone that could understand me or understand what I'm going through. But you can."

"Go on," Judy urged. She glanced across the room at her daughter to make sure she wasn't listening, but Kate was still happily engrossed in Barbie world.

"For the record, I'm not married. But the father of my child, Steven, is a drug addict. He doesn't work. We've been living with his mother for almost two months, and I think it's just a matter of time before he ends up in jail." Tammy took a deep breath. She had just opened the gates to her troubled personal life and let someone in for the very first time. The emotions flooding through her were exhilarating; a feeling of hope and a sense of release. She felt like she'd just unblocked a valve and all the built-up pressure was bursting to freedom.

No longer feeling alone in her nightmare, she now had someone to talk to and share it with. Tammy folded her arms and embraced herself with the new comfort she was experiencing. "When I look at you, I see me. I see myself living here with Matt. But I must confess, unlike you, I can't tolerate Steven's lifestyle. I want to leave him. Even though he's my son's father, I'm afraid for our safety. He's been violent toward me in the past. If I stay, I truly believe he's more than capable of doing serious harm to the both of us."

"Oh, wow..." Judy was shocked. She had no idea Tammy was hiding such a secret. "Dave, my kids' father, isn't a violent man. He's never raised his voice or his hand to me or the kids. There are many nights, though, where I've held my kids tightly and cried alone while my husband is hauled off to jail...again. He's a drug addict, yes, and I feel sorry for him. He truly wants to quit and I believe him when he says he does. I tell myself that, one day; he'll beat this addiction and be the husband and dad he truly wants to be. I must hold onto that dream. It's what keeps me going, which is why I'm always here when he gets out. If he ever hit me or the kids, though, I'd be gone in a heartbeat."

Kate trotted back across the room, climbed onto her mother's knee, and nestled in her arm. Judy kissed her daughter's head before turning back to Tammy. "Why not see if they have a room available here? You said you liked it."

Tammy beamed. "I would love to live here. Anything's better than living with Steven's mum. Every day, I have to watch her own son constantly harass her for money. She has no clue what's going on. In her eyes, Steven's an angel. I can't bear to watch it anymore."

"Well, if you want, we can go down to the office and ask if they have any vacancies."

"Really?" Tammy said excitedly.

"Sure, I'll take you as soon as Christopher wakes up. In the meantime..." Judy leaned over and tickled Kate. "I need to feed this little girl."

Kate giggled, got up from her knees and followed her mother to the counter, where Judy made a peanut butter and jelly sandwich for Kate, and a cup of coffee for herself and Tammy.

Tammy left the Clifford Motel feeling hopeful. In the matter of an afternoon, everything was falling into place. She got the last room available on the second floor. It was identical to Judy's with two beds, a small fridge, cooker, microwave, and a bathroom—everything included but without the clutter. Fearing it may soon be rented, she'd jumped on it and took the room for one hundred fifty dollars a week, paying a week's rent in advance.

Judy also took her to meet her babysitter, Marie, a nice Hispanic woman who spoke good English. Tammy liked her right away. She had the experience and offered many references. Best of all, her rates were affordable. After discussing her hours, Marie agreed to watch Matt once she had settled in.

Already late for picking up Matt, Judy walked Tammy down to her car, accompanied by Christopher in her arms and Kate holding tightly onto her hand. The rain had finally stopped and people were beginning to filter out of their rooms with their kids. "I'm forever grateful for your help. In one afternoon, my life has completely changed for the better, and I owe it all to you."

"You're welcome. I'm looking forward to having you for a neighbor. We can help each other."

"I'm at your mercy," Tammy said with a laugh.

Tammy leaned in and gave Judy a light hug, being careful not to squish her son. "Bye. And, again, thank you." Before stepping into her car, she knelt in front of Kate. "Bye, Kate."

"Bye," Kate replied before hiding behind her mother again. Tammy laughed at the shy little girl.

Driving home, Tammy's thoughts turned to Steven. The last obstacle left before she could move. How was she going to handle him? She didn't want a scene in front of Matt or his mother. Tammy was certain Steven wouldn't want to leave the comforts of his mother's home or, more importantly, her money.

But would he let her leave? She had the idea to leave before he returned home but soon scratched it, knowing he would only show up at her work the next day and cause chaos. She couldn't risk losing her job. The only option she had was to tell him when his mother was present; in the hope Elizabeth would be able to keep him calm. Tammy shuddered as she imagined what his reaction might be.

After picking up Matt, Tammy headed home to share her news with Elizabeth. Bounding through the front door, Tammy was shocked when she found Elizabeth sitting on the couch, sobbing into a white cotton handkerchief. Still cradling Matt in one arm,

Tammy rushed to her side. "My goodness, Elizabeth. What's happened?"

Her crying intensified as Tammy wrapped her free arm around her shoulders. In between sniffles, Elizabeth wiped her eyes and said, "Oh, Tammy! Steven called me."

"And?" Elizabeth shook her head and cried into her handkerchief again.

"Is he okay?" Tammy asked.

"He's been arrested," she replied. "He's in jail. He said he was arrested for selling drugs. My boy doesn't sell drugs!"

While comforting Steven's mother, Tammy was silently rejoicing. It took all her strength to refrain from dancing across the room and screaming "YES!" out of the window. Unbeknown to Elizabeth, Tammy was thrilled he was locked up—she just hoped it would be for a long time. Now she wouldn't have to listen to his protests. For her, the timing couldn't have been more perfect. The final obstacle had been resolved.

CHAPTER 43

Not wanting to leave Elizabeth while she was so distraught over Steven's arrest, Tammy waited a few days before taking the plunge into single motherhood.

Steven had called collect at his mother's house the day after his arrest. With the security of jail walls safely between them, Tammy told him she was moving.

"So, now that I'm locked up, you decide to move," Steven yelled down the phone. "And what about my mother? You can't leave her by herself," he added, still yelling.

With his mother in her own bedroom, Tammy yelled back, hoping Elizabeth wouldn't hear her. "This has nothing to do with you being locked up. I got the place before I even found out you'd been arrested. Matt and I need our own space. And what about your mother? She's been on her own for years, yet suddenly you're concerned? You're just using that as an excuse. Don't worry, I'll pop in and check on her occasionally, which is more than you've ever done in the past five years."

"And what the fuck is that supposed to mean? Are you telling me I don't care about my mother?"

Tammy rolled her eyes. "Steven, you can interpret it however you want. I'm not going to argue with you. You either like it or you don't. I really don't fucking care anymore." She was done explaining herself to him. "Your mother will be fine. I gotta go."

"Wait, bitch! Don't you hang up on me!"

She'd had enough of his bullying. Placing the phone back on its cradle, she beamed with a satisfied smile.

Steven was charged with the selling of narcotics and being under the influence of a controlled substance. He was sentenced to ninety days in jail and would probably end up serving forty-five.

Within twenty-four hours of being locked up, his withdrawals came on strong. First came the intense headaches, followed by the dizziness and nausea. A few hours later, the shakes began. Steven watched his hands tremble uncontrollably while trying to beat the sweats and his dripping nose. Feeling like his body was being turned inside out, the pain in his gut became unbearable and brought him to his knees, causing him to scream in constant agony.

For the first two nights, he didn't sleep; he tossed and turned in wrenching pain, his calls and cries ignored by the guards. They had seen and heard it all before. Other inmates laughed and told him to take it like a man.

By the end of the week, the pains began to subside and the withdrawals were easier to handle and happened less frequently. Once again, Steven told himself he was done with drugs. God had given him another chance and he was now a new man.

After prying his mother for Tammy's phone number, he called her and explained all about the new person he'd transformed into and swore he'd learned his lesson. Tammy had heard it all before and no longer believed his empty promises. While locked up, he had no choice but to stay sober, but she wasn't convinced he would remain clean once released. The temptations would always haunt him, and the cravings would still exist as a constant reminder of the power drugs had over him. She knew without a doubt that he would eventually cave into that power and would yet again become submissive to the drug. To her, it was just a vicious cycle that she no longer wanted to be a part of.

It's been two weeks since Tammy moved out of Elizabeth's and took up residency in the Clifford Motel. Being away from him was like a breath of fresh air. As the days turned into weeks, Tammy was adapting to and enjoying the role of being a single mother. Gone were the days of having to walk around on eggshells in fear of Steven's mood swings. Her money was hers, and hiding it was no longer necessary. For the first time in such a long time, she had control of her life again and she wasn't going to let anyone take that away. The motel wasn't much, but it was home to her and Matt.

Having Judy close by was comforting. They spent many hours sharing each other's stories and giving one another support, each agreeing how much the fathers were missing out on their kids' lives because of drugs.

Tammy cherished the quality time she got to spend with Matt on her days off, even if parts of those days were spent catching up with the laundry and cleaning the room.

She had just returned from the community laundry room with a basket of clean clothes under one arm and Matt cooing in the other when the phone rang. She placed Matt in his playpen and answered the phone. "Hello?"

"Hi, Tammy. It's your dad."

"Dad! What a surprise. How are you?"

"Good, listen, I have some great news."

Tammy quickly picked up on the excitement in his voice. "You do? What is it?"

"I just received a phone call from The Boston Police Department. You're not going to believe this but..."

Tammy heard her dad choking up on the other end of the line.

Growing impatient and now concerned, Tammy urged him on. "What, Dad? What is it?"

He took a deep breath and said, "Donna has been found."

"What!" Tammy screamed as she fell to her knees in disbelief, consumed by an overwhelming surge of emotions.

"Is she okay? Where is she?" She had so many questions that she couldn't get them out fast enough.

"From what I understand, she's going to be fine. She's in the hospital right now."

"The hospital? Why? What happened?" Tammy needed answers. "Is she going to be okay?"

He took a deep breath before repeating to Tammy what the police had told him. "Apparently, she was found in an alley about a week ago. She was beaten up pretty bad."

"Beaten up? Oh no," Tammy shrieked.

"Calm down, she's going to be okay. I have to tell you, though, whoever beat her up had left her to die. It was a homeless woman that found her and called the police. She had a pretty bad concussion, some broken ribs, and bruises all over her body. At the hospital, she told the police who she was and that she had run away from the children's home five years ago. It was the home that gave my number to the police."

With tears of joy flooding down her cheeks, Tammy gasped. "My god, Dad. She's alive. I can't believe it!" She glanced over at Matt, who was lying happily in his playpen, and smiled through her tears. "Matt, your auntie Donna is alive!" Tammy hugged the phone. "Oh, Dad, I can't tell you how long I've been waiting for this day... to hear the news that she is still alive. With all the years that'd passed, I was beginning to think for sure she was dead, but with no leads from the police and no proof, I just couldn't ever bring myself to believe it."

"I know, Tammy, I had the same thoughts."

"So where has she been all this time? Do the police know? Do they have the son of a bitch that beat her up and left her to die?" She couldn't hide the fury in her voice. How could anyone be so malice to another human being? She just couldn't fathom it. She felt the rage rush through her body. It was the same kind of rage that she continually felt with Steven. The anger and disgust felt the same.

"That's all I know, Tammy. I spoke to her for a little while this morning."

"You spoke to her? How did she sound? Did she sound okay?"

"Surprisingly, yes, she sounded okay. A little weak and emotional of course, but who wouldn't be after what she's been through. She kept apologizing for running away. I told her it doesn't matter. I'm just relieved to have her back in our lives. I'm going to fly out there at the end of the week. I bought your mother a ticket and a hotel room. We'll see her together."

"Thanks for bringing Mom out, Dad."

"No need to thank me. She kept asking about you and Jenny though. I gave your mother the number of the hospital and she'll give it to Jenny. Do you want it too?"

"Yes! Yes, of course I want it. Hold on a sec, let me go find a pen."

"Okay."

Tammy set the receiver on the floor and started hunting for a pen and paper. Matt, who seemed to have sensed the excitement, was beginning to fuss. "Hold on, sweetie, I'll feed you in just a minute." Tammy found a pen and notepad by her bed, grabbed it, and returned to the phone.

"Okay, Dad, I got one. Go ahead."

With her hands still trembling, she carefully wrote down all the information her dad relayed to her. "Thanks, Dad. I'll call her as soon as I've fed Matt and put him down. He's starting to get fussy. I gotta go. I love you."

"Love you too, Tammy. Bye now."

Tammy quickly hung up the phone and set about attending to Matt.

Twenty minutes later, after a good feeding and a diaper change, Matt was sleeping soundly in his playpen, which doubled up as his crib. Confident she would have no more interruptions, Tammy prepared herself to call Donna. Just thinking about it was enough to bring tears to her eyes. For years, she'd anticipated receiving a phone call that Donna had been found dead. Where had she'd been all this time? Why hadn't she called anyone? It didn't make any sense. The only way to find out was to call her. With a quick shake of her head and a deep breath, Tammy composed herself and dialed the number to the hospital.

After two rings, a female voice came on the line. "St John's Hospital, how may I direct your call?"

"Yes, hi, can you put me through to room 202 please," Tammy, asked politely.

"One moment please."

With a racing heartbeat and what felt like a whole swarm of butterflies darting around inside her stomach, Tammy listened to the phone ringing, waiting to hear her voice.

"Hello."

The voice sounded weak and tired, but Tammy recognized it immediately. Pools of tears flooded her eyes. "Donna?"

"Yes."

Unable to hold back her sobbing, Tammy choked up. "Donna, it's Tammy."

"Oh my god! Tammy. I've missed you so much."

"I've missed you too." Unable to hold it together, both girls wept over the phone, unable to speak, unable to breathe, engulfed in pure bliss at the thought they had finally found their sister.

"Where have you been, Donna? What happened to you? I honestly thought you were dead." Tammy had so many questions. "I've missed you so much."

For the next hour, Tammy sat on the floor with the phone

glued to her ear, horrified as she listened to Donna describe the past five years of her life. She began by telling her that, when she ran away from the children's home, she met a man who told her how beautiful she was and managed to coax her into going back to his place with him.

Within less than a few weeks, he had her strung out on cocaine and was pimping her out as a prostitute on the streets of Boston. Because she had nowhere else to go, she became dependent on him for drugs and a place to live. He dictated her life for the next five years, working her every night till the early hours of the morning and keeping all the money she earned. Anything Donna needed, she had to get down on her knees and beg for it. Whether it was a bar of soap or a pack of cigarettes, it didn't matter, he made her plead and pray for it. Fear consumed her morning, noon, and night. Not a day went by where she wasn't slapped or punched across the face or beaten to the floor and kicked in the stomach. She lived with constant reminders that if she ever tried to leave, he would hunt her down and kill her. She meant nothing to anybody and wouldn't be missed.

The night she was found in the alley, he had come to pick up the money she'd made while standing on the street for three hours turning tricks. She'd tried to explain it had been a slow night and she'd made nothing, but he spat in her face and told her he didn't believe her. When she tried to reason with him, he slapped her across the cheek and called her a lying piece of shit. The more she protested and swore she had no money, the more he hit her. As she fell to the ground, Donna recalled, he continued to kick her in the head and stomach until she finally passed out. The next thing she knew, she was waking up in the hospital.

There was silence on the phone. "Tammy, are you still there?"

"Yeah, I'm still here," Tammy replied in a somber tone. "I just can't believe what you've been through."

"I'm so sorry I never called any of you guys. I hope now you can see why. I just couldn't, he would have killed me, I'm sure of it.

Oh, and by the way, I didn't tell Dad any of this. I don't want him to know, so please don't tell him."

Tammy was still having a hard time grasping Donna's horrible story. Still in a daze, she spoke softly. "Yeah, that's fine. I understand. You don't have to worry. I won't say anything. Have you talked to Mum or Jenny yet? Are you going to tell them?"

"No, I haven't talked to them yet but I do intend to tell them. I just don't want Dad to know. Not yet anyway."

"Hey, are you going to file charges against the guy that did this to you?"

"God, no!" Donna said without hesitation. "If I do, he'll probably come looking for me, and he'd make sure I was dead the next time he beat me up. I did give the cops his name and address, but I won't testify. I just want to get as far away from him as possible." Donna hesitated for a moment. "I want to come live with you, Tammy. He'll never find me in California. I'll finally be safe, and more importantly, I'll finally be with you."

Tammy almost dropped the phone in surprise. "You want to come live out here?" She paused. "With me?"

"Yes. I can't stay here. It would be okay, wouldn't it?" Donna asked.

Tammy wasn't about to say no to her sister, especially after what she had been through. She scanned her room, wondering where Donna would sleep. The extra bed was an array of clothes, toys, and groceries. "Yes, yes, of course you can stay with me. Why wouldn't it be okay, silly?" Tammy said with a light chuckle. "When will they release you from hospital?" Tammy needed to know how much time she had to prepare for her arrival.

"I'm not sure. I think in about a week. Do you think Dad will pay for my ticket? He and Mom will be here in a couple of days. I can't wait to see them, but I'm afraid to ask him for anything."

"Of course he will," Tammy assured her. "I'm sure he's not going to let you stay out there all by yourself. Not after what's happened to you. Let me talk to him, okay?"

"Okay...and thanks." The line went quiet. Tammy could hear her sister crying again. "I've missed you, Tammy. There were so many times I wanted to call you, but I was too scared." Donna sniffled into the phone. "He would have killed me if he found out. I'm really sorry for not calling you or the others. Can you forgive me?"

"Of course I can. Why don't you get some rest, and I'll call Dad to see when we can get you out here, okay?"

"Okay. I love you, sis." "I love you too, sis. Bye, I'll talk to you soon. And, Donna?" "Yes?" "Welcome back," Tammy said with a smile. "Thanks, it's good to be back." After hanging up, Tammy held the phone in her shaking hands as if she were embracing her long-lost sister. She was unable to hold back the intense tears of joy that drenched her face. After all these years of questions, concerns, and heartbreak, she was about to see her sister again. She was alive but had been living a nightmare. Tammy glanced over at the playpen and was relieved to see Matt was still sleeping, which meant she had time to make a few more phone calls.

After pulling herself together, Tammy called her father. He answered the phone almost right away. "Hello?"

"Hi, Dad, it's me again." "Hey, Tammy. Did you talk to Donna?"

"Yes, I did. Gosh, it was wonderful to hear her voice. I'm so happy she's okay. Anyway, the reason I'm calling is, um, she wants to come live out here. She doesn't feel safe in Boston. I can't say I blame her. So, we figured she could come live with me."

"That's a brilliant idea," John replied, clearly elated.

"Yeah, I think so. Anyway, Dad, is there any chance you can buy her a ticket? She has no money and I certainly can't afford to buy one."

"Of course! Consider it done. I'll let you know the details in a day or so."

"Thanks, Dad. You're the best."

They continued to share their joys of Donna's return for a few more minutes before saying their goodbyes and hanging up. Tammy was left with the unbelievable realization that, in about a week, she would be seeing Donna, her beloved sister, for the first time in years.

CHAPTER 44

That evening, Steven attempted to call Tammy, but she refused the collect call. It had been such an amazing day with Donna now back in her life, not to mention the anticipation of seeing her next week, so there was no way she wanted it ruined by him.

Three days later, he called again. Tammy was rocking Matthew to sleep, but she reluctantly had the call put through. As soon as it was connected, she was deafened by Steven's joyous squeals. "Tammy, baby, it's me. I'm out. Come pick me up."

Shocked, Tammy's body instantly became rigid. "You're out? But you've only done five weeks. How is that possible?"

"I know. I can't believe it either. Apparently, they're over-crowded, and I'm one of the lucky ones they let go." He chuckled. "Anyway, just come get me, baby. I have no money for a bus, so I'm standing outside the jail and I'm freezing my ass off."

Tammy's heart sank to the floor. Still fearing him, she had no choice but to give him a ride. "Okay, but I need to get Matt dressed. I'll be there in about an hour."

"Okay, I can't wait to see you. I love you," Steven shouted down the phone. Tammy hung up without replying. She could pretend some things for the sake of her own sanity, but she couldn't pretend to love him anymore. She would never say those words to him again.

"Fucking great," Tammy barked after placing Matt in his playpen. She tossed various items into his diaper bag as she continued her rant. "He's not living here. I won't have it! This is my place. I paid for it and he's not going to bloody well ruin it for me again. As far as I'm concerned he can go live with his mother." She turned to Matt. "Right, Matt?" Her son smiled and cooed at her, kicking his feet in a happy gait. His sweet innocence instantly melted her heart; he had a funny little way of unknowingly comforting her when she needed it the most. She smiled back at him, gently gathered him in her arms, and kissed his tiny forehead. "Come on, big boy, let's get your stupid dad."

An hour later, she pulled up in front of the jail. Before she'd even had chance to park, she spotted Steven galloping toward her car. The streetlights illuminated his scruffy wardrobe, consisting of black sweats, a stretched out gray sweatshirt, and a pair of slip-on sandals over his bare feet. As he approached the car, she began to fully appreciate his fresh-out-of-jail appearance. He looked awful. His hair was matted and dirty and in dire need of a good brushing. A short, scruffy black beard hid his chin, and his ever-present mustache needed a generous trim. His taut, pallid skin stretched over his prominent cheekbones; an indication of his drastic weight loss.

As he stepped into the car, he glanced over at his son who was sleeping soundly in his car seat. He then turned to Tammy and gave her a peck on the cheek. She quickly turned her head and covered her nose as she reached for the car window handle. "God, Steven, you stink!" she yelled, winding down the window as if her life depended on it. Taking in a lungful of fresh air, she gladly welcomed the cool breeze from outside.

"Geez, sorry, Tammy, not exactly the Ritz Carlton in there you know. Come on, let's go home so I can take a shower."

Tammy pulled away from the curb with a huge smile on her face. "I have some great news," she said.

"Oh yeah, what's that?" Steven asked while fidgeting with his sandals that had slipped off.

"My sister Donna has been found. Can you believe it? She's coming out here in three days. I'm so excited, I can't wait!"

"Wow! That's awesome, Tammy. Didn't I always tell you she was going to be okay?"

"Yeah, you did," Tammy agreed, avoiding eye contact, knowing what his next question was going to be.

"Where's she staying?"

With her eyes fixed on the road ahead, she gripped her hands firmly on the steering wheel. "With me," she replied, loading her voice with as much confidence as she could muster.

"What? The place you have ain't big enough for three people and a baby."

"You're right, it's not. Which is why I need you to stay with your mother."

"What? I just got out of jail for fuck's sake! What the fuck are you talking about? Live with my mother."

Tammy tried to reason with him, only for the sake of not wanting to start a fight with Matt in the car. "It'll only be for a little while. My sister has been through a lot, Steven. I just want to help her out and get her back on her feet."

"What about me? I've been through a lot, too, you know? I just got out of fucking jail!" He thought for a moment. "Wait. Are you dumping me?"

Her immediate reaction was to yell "YES!" at the top of her voice and be rid of him once and for all. But, once again, she told him what he needed to hear in order to keep him calm. "No. I'm trying to help my sister, that's all."

Steven shuffled in his seat. He really wasn't keen on the idea of going back to live with his mother. But, in reality, what was more important right now, what he really needed, was a fix. Staying with his mother would be easy money. Especially tonight, with the novelty of having her beloved son back home after the injustice of being locked up for something he didn't do. He was exhausted and wasn't up to hustling. His mother was a perfect alternative.

"Fine. Take me to my mother's. I'll see you tomorrow," Steven said, pretending to feel like he'd had his nose pushed out.

Tammy wasn't about to argue with him. Getting him to stay at his mother's had been easier than she'd thought. Beneath her mask of anger and hatred, she was glowing with endless delight and self-satisfaction. She sped up a little bit and happily waved goodbye as she left him standing in the parking lot outside his mom's place.

CHAPTER 45

The day Tammy had relentlessly hoped and prayed for over the last five years had finally arrived. She was pulling into the busy Terminal Six parking lot at LAX airport to pick up Donna.

Thankfully, she had only seen Steven once since he was released from jail. He'd turned up at her apartment two days ago; using the excuse he wanted to see Matt. Tammy wasn't surprised to see he paid no attention to him once inside the room. She noticed right away he was high, showing the usual signs of dark, sunken eyes, the smirk, and the occasional nod while sitting. She'd also caught him scouring the room. "There's nothing of value here, Steven," she'd warned.

"What are you talking about?" he said defensively. "I was just checking out the place. Give me a break."

"Yeah, right. You'd sell the shirt off my back if you could get a good price for it."

"No, I wouldn't. Hey, I'm starving, can you give me some money so I can get a bite to eat?"

Tammy threw out a laugh. "I'm not giving you any money. Do you think I'm that bloody stupid? I have food, go make yourself a sandwich. I'm not falling for your little scheme."

Angered that he couldn't coax her into giving her a few bucks, he'd said a few choice words and left, slamming the door behind him. With all thoughts of Steven pushed to the back of her mind, Tammy concentrated on parking the car. She never believed she'd see the day when she was reunited with Donna. For the past three days, she had thought on nothing else. Tangled up in a ball of emotions from anxiety and anticipation to excitement and joy, she was now nothing more than a bundle of nerves.

After trying on five different outfits that morning, she'd finally settled on a pair of cream-colored pants, matching heels, and a beige silk shirt. She had even splurged and bought Matt a rather expensive pair of denim overalls and a blue and white- checkered shirt along with a matching baseball hat.

Tammy had a million "what if" questions zipping through her mind. What if they didn't get along? What if Donna wasn't how she remembered her? What if Donna didn't like her?

Brushing her fears aside, Tammy smiled at her son. "You always give me strength, Matt, and you help me push myself through my troubles. I love you sooo much." She leaned in and kissed him on his cheek. Matt squealed and laughed. "Come on, big boy, let's go meet your auntie Donna."

Tammy scurried through the covered parking lot while looking in all directions. Cars zipped by her in the hunt for a parking space, others backed out, not paying attention. Twice she banged on the trunks of cars yelling "Hey!" before they almost plowed into her. Once outside, she shielded Matt's eyes from the unwelcome glares of the bright sun. She only enjoyed the heat in moderation and was quickly growing tired of Southern California's constant heat waves. She missed the four seasons. L.A. seemed to have just one: summer all year long.

Tammy spotted terminal six across the road. Lost in the crowd of people waiting to cross, Tammy watched the bustle of tourists, cars and taxis traveling in all directions. Manners simply didn't exist. Cars honked and people yelled and bumped into each other as they rushed to get to their destinations. The airport was a place of confusion, hostility, and rudeness, sparing no consideration for others. Holding Matt tighter, she crossed the road when the light turned green and hurried inside the terminal.

Finding the inside to be a much calmer environment, Tammy breathed a sigh of relief and made her way over to the area of the airport marked as "Arrivals." She stood on her tiptoes to see above the heads of others as she searched the monitors for Donna's flight; it was landing in fifteen minutes. She then followed the signs leading to the baggage claim area. Now at six months old, Matt's weight felt heavy in her tiring arms. She wished she'd grabbed his stroller from the trunk.

Tammy wondered what Donna looked like. Too much time had passed since that now tattered photo of her was taken; the one she carried everywhere in her wallet. Donna had told her that her hair was now long and dyed blond, which Tammy had a hard time picturing. For the purposes of spotting each other in the airport, Tammy let Donna know her hair was still red and still the same style. Wavy, shoulder length, and feathered bangs.

For the next forty-five minutes, while bouncing Matt on her knees, Tammy anxiously waited for Donna to appear. She honed her eyes in on every blond female that walked through the gate, searching for some sort of recognition. After frantically scanning what felt like hundreds of arriving passengers, finally, she saw her. Donna spotted Tammy at the same time. They both gasped. Donna froze. With Matt resting on her hip, Tammy rose slowly from her seat, raised her hand high in the air and waved hysterically. Donna waved back and broke out a smile, tears swelling in her eyes. Her nightmare had finally come to an end. She was safe. Jordon could no longer hurt or threaten her. Ready to start her new life, Donna quickened her pace as she approached her baby sister.

Face to face, Donna looked skinny, wearing a tight black mini dress, black nylons, and black high heels. Tammy suddenly felt like a bit of a plain Jane in her boring beige suit. Donna's makeup was heavy, with a thick layer of mascara, a ruby-red lipstick painted perfectly over her lips, and a matching red nail polish disguising her badly chewed nails.

"Donna!" Tammy squealed.

"Tammy!" Donna screamed back. Embracing her sister with her free arm, Tammy held Donna tight against her.

"Oh, I've missed you so much."

"I've missed you too," Donna cried in between her gush of tears. After a few moments of not wanting to let go of their long awaited reunion, they finally parted. Still holding hands, both sisters took a step back to absorb the glorious sight of each other. Neither could believe they were actually standing face to face with the other.

"You look good, Donna."

"So do you, sis." Tammy turned her hip so Matt was facing her sister. "This is your nephew. His name is Matt. Matt, meet your auntie Donna." Donna reached out and squeezed Matt's cheek. "Hi, Matt. You're so frigging cute!" She looked at Tammy. "Can I hold him?"

"Of course you can." Tammy leaned into Donna and bundled Matt into her arms. Never having held a child before, Donna felt a little awkward at

first but soon warmed up when Matt shone her a huge smile. "Oh, you're so precious. It's so nice to meet you, Matt." Donna glanced over at Tammy. "I can't believe you're a mother."

"It's an amazing feeling, and so is watching aunt and nephew meet for the first time." Tammy beamed with pride. "Now, come on, let's go get your luggage," she said while locking arms with her sister and chuckling. "I'll let you have the pleasure of carrying Matt."

"It will be my pleasure."

～

Over the next few weeks, the two sisters spent endless hours catching up on their lost five years. Tammy hadn't noticed over the phone, but Donna no longer spoke with an English accent. For entertainment purposes, she had tried speaking with one but had failed miserably.

Donna recalled how she'd shared a tearful reunion with their father and mother at the hospital. Tammy laughed when Donna told her that Mom had refused to stay at the hotel when she arrived. Instead, she had insisted on sleeping on a cot in Donna's room until she was well enough to be released.

Donna went on to tell Tammy that, after she'd left the hospital, they all stayed at the hotel and Mom and Dad treated her like a queen. They both took her shopping and bought her an entire wardrobe, and Mom even took her to have her hair done. For Donna, the three days at the hotel went by far too quickly. She shared with Tammy how saying goodbye at the airport had been really tough. She desperately wanted to spend more time with them but understood Mom and Dad had to get back to their lives. More importantly, she had a new one to begin in California.

Donna choked up when she talked about her emotional reunion over the phone with her twin, Jenny, and discovered she had missed her wedding. They had talked for hours. Donna understood that Jenny couldn't take time away from her work—caring for the elderly—at such short notice without jeopardizing her job or losing pay. "As soon as my status is sorted out here in the States, I promise I will come visit you and Mom in England," Donna had told Jenny.

When Donna spoke of Jenny, sadness crept over Tammy, too. She hadn't seen her since she'd left England. They wrote occasionally and exchanged photos, but the distance between them had grown. In some ways, Tammy felt she had found one sister but lost another.

Tammy explained to Donna that the motel was temporary while Steven looked for work and that Steven was staying with his mother so she could stay with Tammy.

Donna wasn't convinced that Tammy was telling her everything.

After meeting Steven for the first time, which consisted of a brief fifteen-minute visit where he was oblivious to his son playing in the playpen and herself reading a magazine on the bed, Donna's instincts had been proved right. She'd seen enough drug addicts to recognize one when she saw one.

With only one mission in mind, Steven had pulled Tammy outside to exchange some private words. Donna couldn't hear the entire conversation, but she knew what they were discussing. He wanted money from her. Stand your ground, sis, don't give into him, Donna thought when she overheard Tammy say "NO" in a strained, loud whisper.

"Why not?" she heard Steven ask, his voice frustrated.

Donna sat up to listen more closely. If Steven became violent, she was ready to rush out and butt in. She'd had her fair share of being bullied and wasn't about to let it happen to her sister. Fortunately, there was no need. Tammy had stood her ground and re-entered the room while Steven, she assumed, had left. Probably racking his brains and trying to think who else he could hit up for money.

"Okay, Tammy, what's going on?" Donna asked in a stern voice.

"What do you mean?" asked Tammy, checking on Matt as a distraction.

"Oh come on, Tammy! He's on drugs. He was high as a kite. I've been around the block a few times so I know when someone is using drugs. So, what's the deal? What's going on? Is that why you're living in this dump? Because of his drugs?"

Tammy knew she could no longer fool her sister. "Yes, he has a drug problem." But then found herself defending him yet again. "But he's trying really hard to quit."

Donna rolled her eyes. "You honestly believe that? Are you that stupid? If you keep allowing him to come around, he's gonna keep harassing you for money. Jeez, Tammy, wake up!"

Tammy knew she was right, but she still continued to make excuses. "I know that, Donna, but I have his child. I don't want Matt to grow up without a father."

Donna tried desperately to talk some sense into her sister. She knew Tammy was fighting a losing battle. She had seen the same scenario repeatedly back in Boston. Many of the other prostitutes had children and were trying to support not only their kids but also the dad, who was invariably a drug addict or an alcoholic.

She looked directly into her sister's eyes and spoke sternly in a louder voice as a serious look blanketed her face. "This is no joke, Tammy. Quit defending him. He's a deadbeat dad. What has he ever done for you and Matt? What do you mean when you say you don't want Matt to be without a father? He'd probably be better off without him. I can't tell you what to do, Tammy, but I can tell you what I think, and I think you're a fool if you stay with him."

Tammy lowered her head in shame, embarrassed that Steven was Matt's father; not that she would ever admit it. Even though she no longer had feelings for him, it wasn't that easy to just pack up and leave. Donna didn't know that he'd threatened to hunt her down and kill her if she left him, and she wasn't about to tell her, either. This is something she was just going to have to figure out on her own.

"It's not that simple, Donna. You don't understand." She didn't want to have this conversation. Not now. "Listen, can we talk about this later. I have a bad headache. Can you watch Matt for a half hour? I'm going to take a bath."

"Sure. But taking a bath ain't gonna solve your problems," Donna said sarcastically.

For the first time since Donna arrived, Tammy raised her voice at her. "Damn it, Donna! I said *not now*. Can we just drop it please?" Tammy glanced at the playpen when she heard Matt beginning to stir. He gurgled a few times and then went back to sleep. She lowered her voice. "When I'm ready, I'll do something. Now is not the right time."

"It never is, baby sis. It never is."

CHAPTER 46

ammy eventually shared her troubled times with Donna and confessed that Steven was a heroin addict. She told her about his lying and stealing and how she struggled to make ends meet by spending money she'd worked hard to save. She confided in her about her fears of walking away and what he may do to hurt her and Matt if she did.

Donna understood her fears. She, too, had been waiting for the right moment and building up the courage to escape her pimp so she could take her life back. In the end, he had done it for her; albeit by almost killing her and leaving her to die in an alley. She didn't want that to happen to her sister. It seemed Tammy needed her as much as she needed Tammy, and Donna was determined to find a way to get her and Matt away from that monster of a man.

Although Tammy never complained about taking care of Donna, feeding her, or buying her clothes at thrift stores, Donna didn't want to be a burden and wasted no time in finding a job. Her choices were limited, having run away as a minor and never becoming legalized in the States. She walked up and down the streets of the neighborhood when Tammy was at work and, within a week, was hired as a stripper at a club a few blocks away.

"A stripper!" Tammy screeched in shock when she heard the news. "Couldn't you find anything better? How can you even do that?" she asked, horrified by the thought.

"What choices do I have, Tammy? I'll tell you something, it's a lot safer than turning tricks on a corner and having to answer to a goddamn pimp. It's a legit business. They have security, and the girls' welfare is always a top priority. How do I do it, you ask? After a few beers, I loosen up. I become numb and I just do it. Do I enjoy it? No. It's a job that pays well and will give me some independence. It's all I can do right now, and I'm sorry if you don't like it but there's nothing else I can do," Donna said defensively.

Tammy instantly felt guilty. "I'm sorry, I have no right to judge you."

Donna was right. It was a vast improvement from turning tricks on the street and, much to Tammy's surprise; she made more than a decent enough living. Tammy welcomed the help Donna offered with rent and food, something she'd never experienced with Steven. In addition, Donna was able to save some money in the hopes of getting her own place someday. Tammy objected profusely when she discovered she was stashing the savings in her suitcase.

"I really wish you'd let me keep your money in my bank where it'll be safe," Tammy pleaded as flashbacks of finding the empty envelope zipped through her mind.

"It's fine in here. It ain't going nowhere. Besides, if I need some, I don't have to bother you to go to the bank. Don't worry about it. Okay?" Donna said as she closed the suitcase and pushed it back under the bed.

Donna had come a long way in the short time she'd been in California. Tammy admired her strength and how she'd managed to pick up the pieces of her broken life so she could live life on her own terms. She was proud of her. But Tammy got some unexpected news when Donna returned home one night, carrying a bouquet of roses.

"Wow! Aren't you special. Who's the lucky guy?"

Donna pranced into the room like a teenager experiencing her first crush. "His name is Jason and he's gorgeous. He works as a ranch handler somewhere outside the city. He's strong, muscular, and beautifully tanned. I spotted him as soon as he walked into the club. I was pretty stoked when he asked me out," Donna announced, followed by a glorious laugh. "I've been seeing him for a few weeks and it's amazing. Tammy, I'd never been on a real date before. It felt awkward at first. I was expecting him to throw dollars at me." Donna laughed again. "But he treats me like royalty. I think I'm falling in love with him."

"That's great, Donna." Tammy smiled, genuinely happy for her sister. "How come you've never told me about this guy?"

"I dunno. I didn't know where it was going at first, I guess. Anyway, I'm telling you now. Be happy for me, sis."

Tammy walked over and hugged her sister. "Donna, I'm over the moon. If anyone deserves to be happy, it's you. Here, hand me those flowers and I'll put them in a vase for you."

Within a month, the relationship between Steven and his mother had become strained to the point where Elizabeth was insisting he leave. Having more than outstayed his welcome, and with his mother beginning to see the dark side of her son, she ceased giving him money. In desperate need to feed his addiction, Steven started paying Tammy surprise visits to her work every day. Knowing she wouldn't want a scene, he had been successful in demanding some cash out of her every time.

But his luck was about to change. Tammy was walking round the corner from the kitchen one day when she saw her manager, Paul, meet Steven at the entrance of the restaurant. Tammy ducked back behind a doorway to watch from a distance. Blocking the doorway with his full rounded body, Paul prevented Steven from entering. Paul glared at him, expressing only anger. "I know exactly what you're up to. Tammy may be afraid of you, but I'm not. I've watched you come in here every day, tormenting her and taking money from her," Paul snarled.

"Hey, man, Tammy's my girl, and it ain't none of your fucking business, okay?" Steven snapped back.

Paul leaned forward within inches of his face. "Yes, it is my business when you come in here and upset my waitress while she's on my floor. I make it my business. You got that, punk?"

Steven took a step back. "If my old lady wants to give me money, that's up to her, not you. Who the hell do you think you are?"

"Listen, asshole! I don't want to see your scrawny assed face around here ever again. You got that? If I do, I'm calling the cops and having you arrested. Now get the fuck outta here, you fucking jerk!"

Steven kicked open the door to the restaurant and left in fury— empty handed. Now what was he going to do? Tammy had been his last resort. As he stomped off down the street, it came to him. He had an idea. He knew how he could get some money and get it fast.

CHAPTER 47

*B*efore Steven stormed off, Tammy knew he'd spotted her because he threw her a menacing stare over Paul's shoulder. Tammy quickly turned the other way. For a few minutes, Paul stood by the open door to make sure Steven had left the property. Once confident the bastard was gone, he closed the door and approached Tammy. Noticing she was shaken by Steven's presence, he gently placed his hand on her shoulder. "Are you going to be okay? I eighty-sixed the guy from the restaurant. If he ever steps foot in here again, I'll have him arrested."

"Yeah, I'll be fine. I'm really sorry, Paul. I've told him so many times not to come here."

"Tammy, there's no need for you to apologize. This is not your fault. You need to get away from that guy. He's no good for you. If he causes any trouble for you tonight, you come right here. Do you understand?"

Tammy was touched by his offer. "Thanks, Paul. I'll keep it in mind, I promise."

After seeing the rage in Steven's eyes, Paul was concerned for her safety. "Make sure you do, okay? We're here for you. All of us.

Why don't you take a ten-minute break? I'll have the other girls cover your shift."

"Thanks, Paul. I think I will," Tammy said before giving him a hug.

When Tammy finished her shift, Paul reminded Tammy to come back to the restaurant if Steven gave her any trouble.

She picked up Donna from the club on her way home and listened patiently as she dominated the whole conversation, giving Tammy no chance to tell her about Steven. "Guess what?" Donna asked.

"What?"

"Jason has asked me to move in with him! Can you believe it?"

Tammy faked her happiness. After seeing Steven's outburst, the thought of being alone terrified her. "That's great. When are you moving?"

"I haven't given him an answer yet. It's all happening too fast, don't you think?"

Tammy released a subtle sigh of relief, knowing she was going to be around at least a little while longer. "Yeah, you're probably right. Don't rush into anything," she said as she pulled into her parking space. "Hey, I gotta pick up Matt from the sitter. I'll see you at the room, okay?"

"Okay. Love you, sis," Donna replied as she skipped out of the car and blew her a kiss.

A few minutes later, with Matt in her arms, Tammy headed back to her room. As she neared the apartment, she could see the door was wide open and she could hear Donna yelling from inside. "What the fuck?" Tammy mumbled to herself as she tightened her grip on Matt and hurried toward the door.

Rushing inside, she gasped. Tammy couldn't believe what she was seeing. Her room had been trashed. Everything that could be broken, was. Dishes, chairs, the table; even the mirror above the sink had been shattered. Any items of value had been stolen. The toaster oven, the microwave, and the radio were all gone. She noticed the TV was still there, but only because it belonged to the motel and was bolted to the wall. Tammy stood in the doorway in disbelief, looking at all her wrecked belongings. Donna was knelt on the floor next to her open suitcase.

"Oh my god! What the hell happened?" Tammy cried.

"I'll tell you what fucking happened. Some motherfucker broke in here and stole all my money. Six hundred fucking dollars! It's all gone."

"Oh my god, no! It can't be." Tammy panicked and began scouring the piles of clutter around the room while still holding Matt. "It must be here somewhere."

Donna slammed the suitcase shut and jumped to her feet. "Nope, it's all gone. What the fuck am I going to do now? That was all the money I had." Stepping over broken toys and dishes, Donna sat on the edge of the bed. "Who would do this to you? You have a child. Couldn't they see all the baby things around? And another thing, what the hell does everybody do around here? Didn't anyone see someone break in? Didn't they hear anything when the place was being turned upside down?"

Tammy went silent for a moment, on the verge of tears. "I don't think anyone thought we were being robbed, Donna."

"What do you mean?"

"Think about it. There was no sign of a break in. No windows or locks were broken. Whoever came in here knew how to pick a lock and has been seen here before. I bet you Steven knows how to pick a lock and break in without causing suspicion. People have seen him here, so why would they suspect anything?

"And you think he did this?"

"No, I don't think he did this. I know damn well he did this." Tammy sat of the edge of the bed with Donna and placed Matt between them with a few unbroken toys. She stared in disbelief at the mess surrounding her. How could he do this? she thought.

"He's a drug addict, Donna. He'll do anything for a fix. It doesn't matter who he hurts, his mother, you, even Matt, or me.

He's out of control. You've been around them, so you know. Today, he came by my work, which he has been doing all week, by the way. He usually corners me and demands I give him some money. He knows I'm not going to cause a scene and that I'd rather cower and give it to him so he will go away. Well, today, my boss intervened. He stopped him at the door and wouldn't let him come in the restaurant. In fact, he eighty-sixed him and threatened to call the cops if he ever showed up again."

"Wow! You never told me he was harassing you at work."

"I tried to on the way home today, but you were so excited about Jason I didn't want to put a damper on your mood. Anyway, I saw the anger in his eyes when he left. He looked directly at me and stared me down. It scared me, Donna. He came here in a rage and stumbled on your six hundred dollars in the process. I plan on paying you back, by the way."

"No you will not!" Donna insisted. "You didn't steal it. It's not your responsibility. It's my own fault for leaving it here. You kept telling me to put it in the bank. I should have listened to you." Donna picked up Matt, who was beginning to fuss. "But what are you going to do? This was your home. It's destroyed. I can go live with Jason, but I can't leave you here like this."

Tammy squeezed her sister's hand as tears rolled down her cheeks. "I'll be fine. My boss said he would help me. I'll go talk to him in the morning. It's over between Steven and me. I'll never forgive him for this. For what he did to our home and even more so for what he did to you." Tammy's crying intensified. "I'm so sorry, Donna, please forgive me."

Donna wrapped her free arm around her baby sister and let her cry. "Shh, it's okay. It's not your fault. Come on, it's almost dinnertime and Matt's hungry. Why don't I take you guys out for dinner and we can figure out what we're going to do about this mess, hmm?"

CHAPTER 48

Over dinner, Donna called Jason and told him what had happened. He insisted they all stay at his place for the night. Not wanting to go home or be alone with Matt, Tammy gladly accepted his offer.

After a sleepless night of worry, wondering what on earth she was going to do, Tammy woke early, bundled up Matt, and left before Donna and Jason appeared. She left a thank you note on the kitchen counter and wrote that she'd be in touch soon.

Her first mission was to find a phone booth and have it out with Steven. Within two minutes, she spotted one on her right and pulled up alongside it. She turned to check on Matt and saw he was sound asleep and opted to leave him in the car while she made the call. Reaching over, she pulled Matt's blanket up under his chin, grabbed her keys, and stepped out of the car. After entering the call box, she peered through the glass to check she could see Matt clearly. With nowhere else to go, Tammy assumed Steven would be at his mother's and dialed her number. A sleepy male voice answered the phone. "Hello?"

Hearing him made Tammy cringe. "You fucking bastard!"

Tammy screamed down the phone. "You destroyed the only home Matt and I had, and you stole from my sister." She didn't need to wait for a reply; she knew he was guilty. "How could you do this? I fucking hate you!" Tammy hollered in a rage.

Steven didn't even try to deny what he was being accused of. "Well, what was I supposed to do? I have no money. You know damn well I need a fix every day so I don't get sick. My mother won't give me any more money. Your stupid boss banned me from the restaurant. Who the hell does he think he is anyway? Your sister shows up in town and you kick me out. So, yeah, I went over to the motel to see what I could find. I was sick, Tammy. I came across your sister's money, and yeah, I took it. I needed to get well, but you just don't understand that, do you?"

Tammy was furious. She couldn't believe he felt no remorse and truly believed he had a good reason to do what he did. "You make me sick, Steven. I never want to see you again. That was your son's home. It wasn't much, but it was all he had. All I had. How could you do this to us?"

"Oh, come on, Tammy, I'll make it up to you. I was desperate. I wasn't thinking straight. You're just upset and acting irrational. Everything's going to be okay. You just need to stop acting silly and saying stupid things. Things you don't even mean."

She didn't want to hear any more of his excuses or listen to him trying to make amends. Deciding she was done with him, she slammed down the phone, got back in her car, and drove to her work.

Tammy arrived at the restaurant during the busy breakfast shift in floods of tears. She stood helpless in the doorway, holding Matt tight, unmoved by the many eyes looking her way. From across the floor, Paul spotted her and immediately walked away from his business, shattered by Tammy's distraught demeanor.

"He destroyed our home. I have nothing. I don't know what to do," Tammy sobbed.

Holding out his arms, Paul embraced Tammy in a tight hug.

With Matt sandwiched between them, he tried to console her. "Shhh, it's going to be okay. We're family here. We'll get you some help."

"Thanks, Paul. I'm so sorry, I didn't know where else to go. I can't believe he did this."

"Don't apologize. You came to the right place. Now, come on, let's go in the back and get you a hot cup of tea and some milk for Matt. Then we'll figure out what we can do for the two of you."

Word traveled fast through the restaurant about Tammy and her troubles with Steven. Everyone pulled together to help her. Marco, the head chef, made them a breakfast fit for royalty. Louise, another waitress, held an impromptu collection and managed to collect over five hundred dollars.

After the breakfast rush was over, most of the staff joined Tammy in the break room to discuss her options and find out what they could do to help. Already feeling overwhelmed by their generosity and the unexpected donations, Tammy felt she couldn't take any more from them. Ruth intervened her objections. Ruth was the oldest waitress—in her sixties—and like a mother to the rest of the girls.

"Stop with your protests, Tammy. I've thought about this, and I'd like you and Matt to come stay with me for a while."

The rest of the staff cheered at Ruth's invitation, but Tammy quickly silenced them. "Oh, Ruth...thank you, but I couldn't."

Offering a caring smile, Ruth sat next to Tammy and took her hand. "I'm not taking no for an answer. I'd love to have you. You know too well my husband passed away recently, and I gotta tell you, I've been pretty lonely. Having you and Matt around will help me, too. We'll be helping each other."

While Tammy bounced Matt on her knees, Ruth took a hold of his tiny hand and spoke baby talk to him. "What do you say, little fella? Wanna come live with me?"

"Oh, Ruth, I don't know what to say. Thank you so much." Tears of happiness filled Tammy's eyes.

With the decision made that she would be staying with Ruth, Paul had some other concerns and wanted to run them by Tammy. Sending everyone back to their stations and asking one of the girls to entertain Matt, he closed the door to the break room. "I don't want to scare you, but there's a good chance that asshole will show up here looking for you. Even though I kicked him out, he'll still come back. I could call the cops, but he may even wait across the street for you when you've finished your shift. You can't be here when that happens. We need to be able to tell him you no longer work here."

A look of worry crossed Tammy's face. "Are you firing me?"

"No, no, of course not...but Steven will think you were."

Tammy creased her brow. "I don't understand."

"You're going to have to go into hiding for a few months. Stay away from anywhere or anyone you had in common with him, like friends, restaurants, and stores. Like I said, he's bound to come here at some point. And when he does, I'll tell him you never showed up for work one day and I fired you. He may come back a few times, but eventually, he'll get the message and give up."

Tammy shook her head in protest. "Paul, I can't afford to take a few months off."

A sly grin appeared over Paul's face. "Don't you worry. I have it all figured out. This is just between you and me, okay?"

Tammy nodded her understanding.

"I'm going to continue to clock you in every day. That way, you'll still get a paycheck each week. You won't get any tips, but at least you'll get a little money coming in."

"You can't do that," Tammy objected. "You could lose your job if you get caught."

"You're forgetting, Tammy, I'm the boss. My job will be fine. Don't you worry. I'll have you make up the hours when you return. We'll work something out."

She rose to her feet. "Thank you, Paul. I owe you one."

Wanting to protect her, Paul wrapped his arms around her. "You're going to be okay. I promise."

After their discussion, Paul left Tammy alone to make some phone calls using the pay phone on the wall. Not wanting her sister to worry, she tried calling her at Jason's first, hoping she was still there.

Thankfully, she was. "Hello?"

"Hey, Donna, it's Tammy."

"Tammy! I've been worried sick about you. I woke up and you were gone. Are you okay? Where are you?"

"I'm fine. I'm at work. Everyone here has been amazing. I'll tell you all about it later. I'm going to be staying with one of the waitresses."

"Tammy, you can stay here."

"Thanks, Donna, but you and Jason are just starting out. I don't want to ruin it for you guys. Having a baby around may scare Jason off." Tammy laughed.

"Okay, if that's what you want. But if it doesn't work out, you're always welcome here. Just remember that."

"I will. Thank you. Hey, listen, I'm going to call my neighbor, Judy, and tell her what happened. I'm hoping she can watch Matt for an hour while I go and salvage what I can from the room. Do you and Jason want to meet me there so you can grab your things? I'd love it if Jason comes in case the asshole shows up."

"Sure, we can do that. What time?"

Tammy thought for a moment. "How about noon?"

Donna agreed to the time and told her she loved her before hanging up the phone.

Just as Paul had predicted, Steven showed up the next day, demanding to know where Tammy was. He was dressed in grunge jeans and a stinky t-shirt that clung to his greasy body. His hair was uncombed and matted and his face was unshaven. Paul felt no pity toward him, only fury. He went along with his plan and told Steven that Tammy never showed up for work and had been fired as a result. After peering around the restaurant in search for her, he bellowed a few choice cuss words and stormed off. The following day, Steven returned. This time, Paul called the cops and had him escorted off the property. After that, he stopped coming by.

~

R uth was the perfect host and welcomed Tammy into her spacious three-bedroom, two-bath home. She gave Tammy and Matt their own bedroom and bathroom, situated at the back of the house, and refused to take any rent. Tammy insisted on paying her way somehow and helped with the groceries and cleaning the house.

Every room was bright and cheerful with yellow painted walls and floral prints on all the drapes, tablecloths, chairs, and couches. Ruth's entire house was a showcase for the many framed pictures of her three daughters, one son, and eight grandchildren.

Tammy enjoyed sharing her evenings with Ruth and listening to her stories about her husband, Jack. Ruth reminisced about how they met and his time in the marines. She told Tammy she didn't have to work, Jack made sure of that, but she still did it for the company and to get herself out of the house.

Most nights, when Matt had gone to sleep, they'd open a bottle of wine and spend the evening playing board games and enjoying each other's company. For once, Tammy felt at ease. She'd forgotten what that felt like. Most of all, she enjoyed spending her entire days with Matt. She was around to watch him take his first steps, learn new words, and try new foods.

Donna and Jason came by frequently for dinner, and Tammy was pleased to hear that, after a month of living with him, Donna had quit the stripping gig and was now living the life of a happy homemaker.

Judy also visited often. Along with Ruth, she kept Tammy in

the loop of any gossip happening at work, but the latest gossip was about Judy herself. Her husband had been released early from jail and took a swing at her the same day. Over money, of course. Judy had packed her bags, got a restraining order on him, and was now living at her mother's with the kids. But she wasn't sure how long she could last.

"Judy, why don't we join forces and get a place together? It would be ideal. I've been at Ruth's for almost two months now. Although she's been fantastic, I can't stay here forever and I need to get back to work. If we ask Paul not to put us on the same shift, we could watch each other's kids. We could seriously help each other out if we did it right."

Judy pondered over her suggestion. "That's not a bad idea. I'm game if you are! I have some money saved. It's not a lot, but if we're splitting everything, I think I can swing it." Judy raised her Coke bottle in a toast and shone a huge grin. "Sure, let's be roommates."

Sitting on the couch together with the kids playing on the floor in front of them, Tammy matched her grin and hugged her soon-to-be roommate. Tammy hoped this would be the last time she'd be starting over. But, with Steven finally out of the picture, everything was on her terms.

That night, Tammy told Ruth about her and Judy's plans. Even though Ruth said she'd be sorry to see her leave, she knew it was time for her to move on. Excited for Tammy, she joined in on their hunt for a new home and insisted they use her as a reference and a co-signer to give them a better chance of finding a place.

All three women spent every spare moment of the next week scanning the classifieds and viewing rentals. By the end of the week, Tammy and Judy were holding the keys to their new two-bedroom, two-bath house in Pasadena, which was a convenient ten-minute drive from work. A three bedroom would have been nice, but with the fenced yard and a quiet street, it was perfect for the kids—and it was affordable. Tammy gave Judy and her kids the bigger bedroom with the en-suite bathroom, and Tammy and Matt took the smaller one with the bathroom at the end of the hallway. The kitchen was spacious with white cabinets, a stove, a fridge, and a large dining area where a table big enough to seat everyone would fit. The living room had French doors overlooking the backyard and a cozy brick fireplace in the corner.

Paul agreed to put them on different shifts, and because Tammy had a car, he gave her the nights. Once again, everyone at work offered to help by donating most of their furniture, including beds for every one, a couch, a dining set, dishes, pots and pans, and toys and clothes for the kids. The only things they needed to buy were a TV and a telephone.

As per Paul's Plan, Tammy had gone into hiding for two months and hadn't heard anything from Steven. The plan had worked. She was now ready to start her new life and was due to return to work in two days. Tammy had agreed with Paul to take a small cut in her hourly wage to begin paying back the funds she was fronted while in hiding.

For the first few days, Tammy's anxiety level was high. Every time the door to the restaurant opened, she spun around and expected to see Steven. But, over the next few weeks, her uneasiness subsided and she began to embrace having normality in her life.

After returning home from a busy dinner shift, Tammy kicked off her shoes and flopped onto the couch like a wet rag.

"You look exhausted," Judy remarked. "Want a glass of wine?"
"Yeah, that sounds great. How was Matt?"

"Oh, he was great as usual," Judy, hollered from the kitchen before returning with two glasses of white wine. "Here you go," Judy said as she handed Tammy a glass and took a seat next to her, placing her glass on the coffee table.

Tammy took a large sip. "Oh, that's good. Thanks."

"You're welcome. Hey, I'm off tomorrow, want to take the kids somewhere?" Judy asked.

"Sure. Do you—"

Judy quickly stood up, interrupting Tammy, and held her hand up in front of her. "Shhh, did you hear that?"

Tammy froze. "No, I didn't. What was it?" she whispered.

"I could have sworn I heard footsteps," Judy said quietly, feeling worried.

Suddenly, a loud crash came from the front door as one of the eight glass panes shattered to the floor. They both shrieked and Tammy jumped up from the couch to join Judy. Terrified, they clung to each other and watched as a gloved hand reached through the white mesh curtain, searching for the lock.

"Oh my god!" Tammy screamed.

Judy broke herself free from Tammy's grasp and grabbed the poker from the fireplace.

"Where are you going?" Tammy screamed.

"Hurry! Call nine-one-one!" Judy yelled back as she raced through the kitchen toward the back door.

"Judy, don't go out there..." But she was gone. While fumbling with the keypad on the phone, Tammy screeched at the intruder, "Go away! I'm calling the police." Not fazed by Tammy's threat, the imposter continued to search for the deadbolt. "I'm calling them right now," Tammy yelled.

A female dispatcher came on the line. "Nine-one-one. Is this an emergency?"

Holding the receiver tight as if it were her only lifeline, Tammy bellowed into the phone, "Someone is trying to break into my house! Hurry! They've broken my door. I have glass everywhere."

"Stay calm, ma'am. Help is on the way," the woman explained in a calm voice.

Still clinging to the phone, Tammy heard a loud thud and then a muffled groan. Staring at the door, she saw the gloved hand disappear back through the broken glass and fall away on the other side of the door. Fearing for Judy's safety, she threw down the phone, leaving the dispatcher talking to herself. Tammy screamed, "Judy!"

Driven by adrenaline, her only concern being her friend, Tammy rushed to the front door. Avoiding the broken glass sprayed across the floor, she unbolted the lock and yanked the door open. Panting and listening to the sound of her pulse beating in her ears, Tammy found herself face to face with Judy. The intruder lay face down on the ground between them. Standing with her feet apart, holding the poker in one hand, Judy released her grip on her weapon and let it crash to the ground.

Tammy raced to Judy's side and held her tight. "Oh my god! Are you okay?" she looked down at the motionless body at their feet. "Jesus, did you kill him?"

"No, I just gave him a good whack across the back of the head and knocked him out cold." Judy smirked as she walked around to the other side of the man and crouched down. "Come on, let's see who this bastard is."

Tammy leaned down on the other side and took hold of the medium-built limp body with two fistfuls of his jacket. With one final shove, they managed to roll him over.

Tammy immediately jumped back. "Fuck...Its Steven!"

Still crouched, Judy took a closer look at the scruffy, bearded face. "Damn. It sure is. I only saw him once when he came into the restaurant to bug you, but even with that beard sprouting out of his chin, I'd never forget that ugly, scrawny face."

Tammy and Judy turned their heads in unison at the sound of sirens coming closer to the house. Judy rose to her feet and approached Tammy with open arms.

"How the hell did he find me?" Tammy said. "He's like a friggin' nightmare that won't go away. What am I going to do? I can't keep running from this creep."

Rubbing Tammy's shoulders, Judy led her over to the steps of the front porch. "Sit here while I go check on the kids. The cops should be here any second, they sounded pretty close."

"Okay." Tammy eased herself into a sitting position against the cool front wall of the house.

Judy returned just as the patrol car pulled up, illuminating the front yard with its flashing lights. "Amazing, the kids slept through the whole thing. They're all sound asleep. I'll be right back. I'm gonna go talk to the cops," Judy said as she scurried to meet the officers stepping out of the patrol car.

Tammy scanned the street while she waited. Neighbors were now standing on their front lawns dressed in pajamas and bathrobes. She spotted others peeking through their curtains. Embarrassed by the scene unfolding in front of her house, Tammy avoided their curious stares.

Moments later, the two officers approached Steven, who was still out cold on the ground. Tammy watched with slight amusement as they brought him to a conscious state by slapping him across the cheeks a few times. "What the fuck!" Steven hollered as he started to come to. Not giving Steven an opportunity to lash out, the two policemen immediately brought him to his feet and handcuffed his hands behind his back. One of the officers led him to their patrol car while the other stayed with Tammy.

"Are you okay?" Judy asked her as she slid down next to Tammy and held her hand.

"Yeah, thanks."

When the officer approached them, both girls stood to greet him. "How are you doing?" the cop asked Tammy.

"I'm okay, just a little shook up."

The cop smiled at Tammy. "Well, you can relax now. He won't be bothering you for a long time. Apparently, he just robbed a liquor store a few blocks from here. We have eyewitnesses. He also has numerous outstanding warrants. He's obviously under the influence of drugs and he's carrying a loaded firearm, which I'm sure he doesn't have a license for. We also now have him for trespassing and breaking and will be charged anyway, whether you do or not."

Tammy shook her head. "No, I just want him to go away. How much time do you think he will get?"

"I'd say at least six years," the officer replied, followed by a smile, knowing he was giving her good news.

With a huge sigh of relief, Tammy let the tears trickle freely down her cheeks. She was finally free of Steven and, without a doubt, she had her life back. She glanced over at the pathetic excuse of a man sitting in the back of the patrol car—a man she no longer knew. A man, whose mind was consumed by drugs. An addiction so powerful that it cost him his family and his son.

Because of their twisted love affair, Tammy had lost one love to drugs, but she gained an even greater one the day Matt was born. She and Judy watched from the porch as the patrol car pulled away. Tammy knew that chapter of her life was closing. It was time to take her life by the reins and turn these reckless beginnings into happier, better endings.

Turn the page to read the first chapter
Better Endings
Book Two

BETTER ENDINGS

CHAPTER 1

ammy tried to open her eyes, but the bright lights from above forced her to quickly close them again. She tried once more, allowing her eyes to adjust slowly to the piercing lights. She could only manage a squint. *Where am I?*

Then she felt the excruciating pain coming from her head. Wanting to rub it and relieve some of the discomfort she was experiencing, she tried to reach up with her right hand but discovered she couldn't move her arm. Something was holding it back. She only heard metal banging against metal every time she tried to move it. Without turning her head, she managed to look down in the direction of her hand and saw with disbelief that she was handcuffed to the rail of the bed.

"What the fuck?" she whispered out loud.

The repetitive beeping noise from her left distracted her thoughts. Even in pain, she managed to turn her head slowly in the direction of the annoying sound. With her eyes now fully adjusted to the lights, she saw she was hooked up to a monitor and an IV.

She scanned the room and saw an empty bed on her right, which was next to a large picture window with the shades drawn.

On the wall facing her was a television mounted up high. To the left of the TV was a door, which Tammy assumed led to a bathroom, and the other door in the room probably led to the way out.

I'm in a frigging hospital. What the hell happened? She scanned the room again. *How long have I been here?*

Confused and in a state of panic, she yelled, "Hello! Hello! Anyone hear me?"

Suddenly, the door opened, and an officer of the law appeared.

"Who are you? And where am I?" Tammy lifted her cuffed hand. "And why am I handcuffed?" she asked, still in a state of confusion.

The officer remained by the door. "You've been in a car accident. I need you to remain calm, until a nurse arrives to check you out," he said, using his tone of authority.

"But why the handcuffs? My head is killing me." She leaned her head back in the pillow, distraught. "What the hell happened?"

"I'll explain everything to you in just a moment." The officer peeked his head outside the door. "Here she comes now," he said, sounding relieved. "I'm going to leave you alone with her. I will be right outside the door."

Once he had left, Tammy's head went into a tailspin. *Car accident? Was anyone killed? God, why can't I remember?*

While deep in thought, the door opened again. This time it was the nurse with a clipboard in her hand. She was an older lady, skinny, and probably in her late forties. She had dark chestnut hair tied in a ponytail, and she gave Tammy a small smile as she approached the bed.

"Hi, welcome back. You've been out for a while." She stood by Tammy's side. "How are you feeling?"

"I am so confused. I remember nothing." Tammy strained to keep her head up. "My head is killing me, I'm handcuffed to this damn bed, and no one is telling me anything. How would you feel?" she replied sarcastically.

"All I can tell you, is that you came in late last night with severe head injuries after being in a car accident." She turned to look at the monitor. "Your vitals look good." She looked down at the chart in her hand. "It says here that you had eleven stitches across your forehead, which is now bandaged. No broken bones and no internal injuries. I don't think you'll be here too much longer." She finished with another comforting smile.

Tammy tried her hardest to remember the night before. "Hey, what's today's date?" she asked.

"January first. Not exactly a great way to start out 1990 now, is it?" the nurse joked, followed by a chuckle.

"It was my birthday last night. New Year's Eve. Oh my god! That's right, I went out with some friends." Tammy closed her eyes, trying desperately to remember the night before. "We went to... oh, god, I don't remember. We went to a few places and drank all night." She cracked a laugh. "Well, I'll never forget my twenty-fifth birthday, that's for sure." Ignoring the pain in her neck, her body stiffened and her eyes grew wide. "Oh, shit! My son! I never went home." She looked over at the nurse, fear consuming her face. "My roommate Judy must be worried sick! I have to call her! She's watching my son."

The nurse tried to calm her. "I'm sure we can arrange for you to call her after the officer has spoken to you. I'm going to call him in now, and then I'll leave you two alone." She patted Tammy's free hand. "I'll see what we can do about that phone call, okay?" The nurse made her way to the door and opened it enough to call through, "Officer, you can come in now." Opening the door for the officer to enter, she stepped outside and closed the door behind her.

Tammy had a horrific thought and wasted no time asking, "Am I going to jail?" She didn't wait for his answer; she had to explain why she couldn't. "I can't. I have a son at home with my babysitter. He's only four," she pleaded.

The officer ignored her question and approached the bed with a stern look. Chilled by his presence, Tammy cowered back against her pillow.

He gave her a speech, in a manner like a father would give to a child. "You are a very lucky young lady. Do you realize you could have killed yourself?" Tammy nodded. "I'm surprised you don't have any more serious injuries," the officer added.

Tammy didn't want a lecture. She needed answers. "Can you please tell me what happened?" She paused and softened her tone. "Am I going to jail?" she asked again.

The officer continued in a stiff voice. "It seems you attempted to drive a vehicle last night while under the influence of alcohol. You apparently blacked out at the wheel and in the process hit five parked cars. When we received the call, you were found unconscious, stooped over the steering wheel with a large abrasion across your head. You were brought here by ambulance, where a blood sample was taken to measure your blood alcohol level. The results showed it to be 0.11, which is above the legal limit of 0.08. Therefore, you are in our custody for driving while intoxicated. Which is why you are handcuffed to the bed."

Tammy listened in disbelief. "Oh my god! I fucked up big time." She wanted the officer to believe her and tried to sound sincere when she spoke. "I honestly thought I was okay to drive, Officer."

He released a slight chuckle—the first facial expression since he had entered the room. "Everyone does, ma'am," the officer told her.

Tammy dreaded asking the next question, but she needed to know. "Can you tell me if anybody else was hurt?" She took in a deep breath. "I didn't kill anyone, did I? Oh, god, please tell me I didn't. I couldn't live with myself if I did."

The officer delayed his answer for a few seconds, letting her stew over the possibility. "Luckily, no one else was hurt. Just yourself."

Tammy held her hand up to her racing heart while briefly closing her eyes. "Oh, thank god," she gasped.

"And, like I said, you're very lucky to be here." He waited for Tammy to compose herself after hearing she hadn't killed anyone before continuing with his report. "Your car is totaled and has been impounded. They had to use the Jaws of Life to remove you from your vehicle, and I'm here to serve you a DUI." He paused for a moment and pulled out a yellow piece of paper from the top pocket of his shirt. "While you've been here, we ran a report on you. You have no priors or outstanding warrants. It seems this is your first offense."

Tammy spoke quickly. "Yes, it is. I've never been in trouble before."

"Because you've had no priors, we are releasing you on your own recognizance."

Tammy let out a huge sigh of relief, knowing she wasn't going to jail. "But," the officer stated, "you have to appear for your arraignment in two days at the court specified on this ticket I'm giving you to sign. If you don't appear, a warrant will be issued for your arrest."

"Oh, I'll be there. I promise," Tammy said eagerly.

"Okay then, before I remove the handcuffs, do you have any questions?"

"Will I be able to drive again?"

"The courts will explain everything to you. Being a first offense, they will probably suspend your license. But get another DUI and they won't be so lenient, and you will go to jail. I can promise you that."

"Oh, Officer, I've learned my lesson. I'll never get behind the wheel drunk again. I promise."

"That's good to hear. Now I'm going to remove the cuffs and I'll need you to sign this citation."

"Okay."

Tammy watched as the officer walked to the right side of the bed and freed her wrist from the cuffs. Feeling relieved, she rubbed her now stiff, tired arm with her other hand.

"Thanks."

"No problem," he said while reaching into his top pocket for a pen. He turned and slid the bed tray in front of her and laid the ticket and pen down. "Here you go. Once this is signed, I'm all done here and the nurse will be in shortly to advise you on when they will be releasing you."

Tammy took the pen, and without reading the citation, signed her name. "Thank you, Officer. I promise you it won't happen again." The officer took the pen, placed it back in his pocket, removed a copy of the citation and gave it to her while holding onto his copy. "I hope not. You have a good day now." He paused and smiled. "Oh, and happy New Year."

Tammy chuckled. "Thanks. You too," she replied as she watched him walk out of the room, leaving her with her own thoughts. She remembered nothing about the accident. She vaguely remembered getting in her car after saying good night to her friend Hailey, a friend from work. Judy, her roommate, and best friend, had offered to babysit so she could enjoy her birthday. Hailey was also a single mother and wanted to take Tammy out after work. Tammy thought of her son. What a terrible mother she was. Poor Matt must be wondering where Mommy was. Not to mention Judy. God, she fucked up this time. She needed to call home and apologize to Judy.

While deep in thought, the same nurse entered the room. "How are you feeling? I hear you've been released from custody. You're a very lucky lady you know."

"Yeah. I know. The cop told me the same thing."

The nurse walked to the side of the bed and checked the vital machine.

"I can't believe how stupid I've been. I'm a mother. I'm not supposed to be acting this way. I feel like such a failure to my son," Tammy confessed.

"I'm sure he's fine. You can use the phone next to the bed to call home. Just dial nine for an outside line then dial the number. I'll be back in a few minutes."

"Thank you! Oh, wait, what hospital am I in?" "Huntington Memorial in Arcadia."

"Okay, thanks." Before the nurse had left the room, Tammy already had the phone in her hand and was dialing home. After three rings, she heard Judy's voice on the other end.

"Hello?" she heard Judy say.

"Judy, it's Tammy."

"Tammy! I've been worried sick about you. Are you okay? Where are you?"

"I was in a car accident last night. I'm so sorry. I feel terrible."

"Oh my god! Are you okay?"

"Yeah, I'll be fine. I totaled my car though. I don't remember anything, and I woke up to find I was handcuffed to the bed."

"Handcuffed?"

"I'll tell you everything when I get home. Is Matt okay? God, I'm a terrible mother."

"No, you're not," Judy said in a harsh tone. "Don't you say that. He's fine. Do you need me to come get you?"

"I haven't been released yet. But I'm sure I will be soon. If you can, that would be great. I'm so sorry." Tammy paused to remember the name of the hospital. "I'm at Huntington Memorial. Thanks, Judy, I owe you one."

"Don't you worry about it. Matt loves going for car rides." Judy laughed. "I'll see you soon."

CONTINUE READING BETTER ENDINGS

ACKNOWLEDGMENTS

I couldn't have written this book without the continued support of my husband *Gordon Grant*. On the days I struggled, he showed me encouragement and with his words of wisdom pushed me through the difficult days. Thank you for believing in me. I love you xoxo

My dear friend *Joanie Barker* who has been waiting for this books for years. Our hours of discussions over coffee about the book has finally paid off. Your friendship is a treasure. Thank you for your amazing support.

Reviews help not only authors but readers too.

If you enjoyed this book please take a moment to leave a review. I will be forever grateful. Thank you.

ABOUT THE AUTHOR

ABOUT THE AUTHOR

Tina Hogan Grant loves to write stories with strong female characters that know what they want and aren't afraid to chase their dreams. She loves to write sexy and sometimes steamy romances with happy ever after endings.

She is living life to the fullest in a small mountain community in Southern California with her husband and two dogs. When she is not writing she is probably riding her ATV, kayaking or hiking with her best friend – her husband of twenty-five years.

www.tinahogangrant.com

ALSO BY TINA HOGAN GRANT

THE TAMMY MELLOWS SERIES

Reckless Beginnings - Book 1

Better Endings - Book 2

The Reunions Books 3

❧

THE SABELA SERIES

Davin - Prequel

Slater - Book 1

Eve - Book 2

Claire - Book 3

Jill - Book 4

❧

Want to be the first to know when Tina has a new release?

Sign up to stay in the loop

Visit the author's website

https://www.tinahogangrant.com

Join Tina's Facebook Group – Read More Books

Made in the USA
Monee, IL
13 January 2024